BRADWELL'S IMAG

# COAL MINING IN SOUTH WALES

Best wishes
from
Ray Lawrence

**BRADWELL**
**BOOKS**

BRADWELL'S IMAGES OF

# COAL MINING IN SOUTH WALES

RAY LAWRENCE

Featuring the last colliery to close in each of the South Wales mining valleys.

BRADWELL
BOOKS

Published by Bradwell Books
11 Orgreave Close Sheffield S13 9NP
Email: books@bradwellbooks.co.uk

The right of Ray Lawrence to be identified as the author of this work has been asserted by him in accordance with the Copyright, Design and Patents Act, 1988.

British Library Cataloguing in Publication Data: a catalogue record for this book is available from the British Library.

1st Edition

ISBN: 9781912060597

Print: Gomer Press, Llandysul, Ceredigion SA44 4JL

Design and Typesetting by: Andrew Caffrey

Photograph credits: Predominantly from the National Museum Wales, John Cornwell Collection with additional images from the Museum collection and other sources, including the authors. All other images credited separately.

Maps contain Ordnance Survey Data
©Crown copyright and database right 2018.

# CONTENTS

# FOREWORD

The great expansion of the Welsh coalfields occurred during the mid-nineteenth century after trials by the British Admiralty proved the superiority of Welsh coal over that of the long-established coalfield of the north-east of England.

By 1874, South Wales was producing around 16.5 million tons of coal annually and people were pouring into valleys such as the Cynon and the Rhondda to work the new steam-coal pits. In 1851 there were 950 people in the two Rhondda valleys – by 1924 there were 167,000!

By 1913 the South Wales Coalfield had reached a peak output of 57 million tons, which was one fifth of all UK coal production. In that year there were 620 mines in South Wales manned by 232,000 miners. By 1924 the number of miners had reached a peak of 271,000.

It didn't last. From the early 1920s until the Second World War, a long industrial recession hit the Coalfield as shipping converted to oil power and foreign coalfields were developed. Between 1921 and 1936, 241 Welsh mines closed and the number of miners fell from 270,000 to 130,000. The only coal-producing area which bucked this trend was the anthracite coalfield to the west, which actually increased output during this period.

The UK coalfields were nationalised on 1 January 1947. In South Wales there were now 135 major collieries, although 124 of these had been sunk during the previous century and were feeling their age. Most of the easier seams had been worked out and modern working practices were rare. In South Wales, only 36 per cent of coal was being machine cut although 64 per cent of production was being mechanically transported. The numbers of miners had been halved since 1921 and the workforce was an ageing one as parents became reluctant to see their sons starting a career in such a run-down industry.

However, nationalisation gave new hope as the new National Coal Board (NCB) was intent on a massive investment in modernisation with 21 per cent of its budget being earmarked for South Wales, even though the area had only 16 per cent of British mineworkers.

The NCB brought about huge changes in coal cutting and transport. New equipment was developed and there was a greater emphasis on safety standards compared to the previous periods. However, the industry could still prove to be a dangerous one: 45 men lost their lives at Six Bells Colliery in 1960 and 31 at Cambrian Colliery in 1965.

Until the late 1950s, employment and production remained steady but, with the challenge of oil from the Middle East and the general decline in the use of coal, there came another round of pit closures. Between 1957 and 1964, fifty collieries closed in the Coalfield. The pace of closures slowed during the 1970s due to the huge increases in the price of oil.

In the 1980s the threat of closures arose again. Earlier pit closures had been reluctantly accepted as alternative employment was available but the mass unemployment of the Thatcher years led to a last great strike in 1984–85. There were 28 pits working in the South Wales Coalfield when the strike began in March, with a workforce of 20,000 miners. In the aftermath of the defeat of the strike there were mass pit closures and by the late 1990s there were more mining museums than working collieries.

This book looks at the last of the South Wales collieries and is a very welcome addition to the literature of a once-powerful industry. Ray Lawrence has been a good friend to Big Pit, always ready to answer some of the (often strange) queries that I come up with. I salute you, comrade!

## CERI THOMPSON
Curator

Big Pit National Coal Museum, Blaenavon

# ACKNOWLEDGEMENTS

My thanks must go to the staff of the **National Museum of Wales** who were involved in providing most of the photographs in this book, to **Mark Etheridge** for his diligence in helping with the selection and to **Kay Kays** and **Sally Donovan** for sorting the proofs out. **Ceri Thompson,** the curator of **Big Pit,** was his usual helpful self and unflagging in his support for this project, and indeed any other that remembers our mining past.

The late **John Cornwell** deserves a special mention. It was his unstinting devotion to recording the collieries of South Wales on film that served as the basis of this book. I can safely say that no other man has contributed more to recording the history of the Coalfield than John.

I also owe thanks to **Gareth Roden**, **Nev Wescott**, **Phil Cullen** and **Roger Tiley** for allowing me the freedom to use their photographs.

I am grateful to **Bradwell Books** for selecting me for this project and for the patience and guidance that they have given me.

## RAY LAWRENCE

Oakdale, August 2018

# INTRODUCTION

The rapidly disappearing humps, bumps and depressions that litter the ground in the South Wales Valleys betray the industrial past of this area. This is a history covered in blood, sweat and tears, triumphs and disappointments, good times and hardships, riots, starvation and prosperity for a few. They are also landmarks to a stubborn race of people who stood up and fought for the rights of a better future for their children.

This was no little backwater tucked away on the west side of the UK. This was the heartland of the Industrial Revolution, a revolution that moulded the modern world and brought Great Britain to the fore as a military and industrial power.

At the height of coal mining in South Wales the Bristol Channel was the busiest waterway in the world. The world's first million-pound cheque was presented at Cardiff's Coal Exchange, and Welsh coal fuelled the ships of the Royal Navy, foreign navies and commercial ships, including the Titanic. Powell Duffryn was the largest coal company in the world and there were Welsh coal depots in such far-flung places as the Seychelles, Kamaran in Yemen, Rio de Janeiro, La Plata, Bilbao, Genoa, Yokosuka and Bombay.

To feed this huge demand there were about 270,000 miners toiling away in the South Wales Coalfield during the early 1920s. Such was the dominance of the industry in the Valleys that two-thirds of the men who lived in them were employed in its collieries, and nearly all the rest were employed on the railways taking the coal to the markets.

That era is now long gone – the closure of Tower Colliery wrapped up that phase of history – but when you gaze at those humps, bumps and depressions please try to imagine the efforts that your forebears put into making them, and why, and you will then begin to view them not as scenes of ugliness but as markers of an age, and of the people who toiled for a better future for us all.

It was a major headache deciding which pits to include in this book. In total I have unearthed 2,800 coal mines of all shapes and sizes in the South Wales Coalfield, and even in the watershed year of 1985 there were 28 NCB mines in operation. The target figure for this volume was 22 mines, plus Lewis Merthyr and Big Pit. We plumped for the last pit to have worked in each of the individual valleys of the Coalfield. Yet even this was not straightforward and little anomalies had to be overcome, with Mardy Colliery representing both the Rhondda Fach and Fawr Valleys, and the same with Marine Colliery and the Ebbw Fach and Fawr Valleys. Abernant Colliery was in an offshoot valley of the Swansea Valley but as far as the NCB was concerned it was a Swansea Valley mine. We chose Aberpergwm Colliery over the Unity Mine due to its Coal Board association, and with both mines 'mothballed' it is still not clear which will be the last to work in the Vale of Neath. In all we present the reader with a very good cross-section of mines from all areas of the Coalfield in what we hope will not only be an interesting and informative read but will connect you to your heritage, and remind you of an industry that was once called, with good reason, **KING COAL**.

This photograph was taken in January 1952 before the colliery was modernised. The Glyncorrwg South Pit is in the foreground with the North Pit behind it. Just visible in the background is the north Rhondda Colliery

**Amgueddfa Cymru - National Museum Wales**

# BACKGROUND

The Industrial Revolution may have been a mere speck in the long history of this planet, but its impact on the human race was without parallel in the history of time. It changed sleepy, rural valleys and wild rugged hillsides into hives of industrial activity as man dug deeper and deeper into the earth to seek out the graves of long-gone tropical forests. The Industrial Revolution created a nationwide demand for coal, and in the quest to meet this need the valleys of South Wales were found to contain some of the world's finest steam coals.

Coal mining that had started on the fringes of the Coalfield then spread into the interior around the 1840s. In 1855 the first steam coal pit in the Rhondda Valleys, Bute Merthyr, was opened, followed by a bewildering number of other collieries that increased coal production tremendously.

Janeiro. In 1851, 20,000 souls lived in Cardiff but due to the expanding coal trade there were 182,000 residing there in 1911. By 1913 the Coalfield was at its zenith, with expansion almost complete, and coal production had peaked at 56.8 million tons, with 232,800 men and boys employed.

## COAL PRODUCED PER YEAR (IN OLD IMPERIAL TONS)

|  |  |
| --- | --- |
| 1855 | 8.5 million |
| 1865 | 12.6 million |
| 1875 | 14.2 million |
| 1885 | 24.8 million |

## COAL PRODUCED AND MANPOWER EMPLOYED

| Year | Coal Produced | Manpower Employed |
| --- | --- | --- |
| 1890 | 29.4m | 109,953 |
| 1895 | 33.0m | 126,199 |
| 1900 | 39.3m | 147,652 |
| 1905 | 43.2m | 165,609 |
| 1910 | 48.7m | 213,252 |
| 1913 | 56.8m* | 232,800 |
| 1920. | 46.2m | 271,161** |

\* Peak production year
\*\*Peak manpower year

Of course, men were required to dig the coal, and the lure of good wages attracted people from all over the UK. The figure for men and boys employed in the mines of South Wales soon passed the 100,000 mark and continued to rise.

In 1910 exports from South Wales amounted to 17 million tons of coal, with deliveries as varied as 20 tons to the Port of Tucacas in Venezuela to 710,694 tons of coal to Rio de

The collieries were becoming huge: the Cambrian Collieries employed 4,113 men, Lewis Merthyr 3,770, Six Bells 3,716, Merthyr Vale 3,575, Llwynypia pits 3,400 and the

Cymmer pits 3,069. Control of the Coalfield was taken over by the government in 1916 and for the first time membership of the South Wales Miners' Federation (SWMF) became a condition of employment.

In 1920 the value of South Wales coal exports amounted to 60 per cent of all UK exports. The peak year for South Wales coal exports was in 1923 when 31.1 million tons of coal were sent to all corners of the globe. Then the bubble burst. Oil was rapidly replacing coal on the ships and railways of the world, the Versailles Reparation Treaty supplied some markets with German coal, and other European nations such as Poland were subsidising their coal in an attempt to gain currency. On top of all this the USA had taken over from South Wales in the markets of South America.

In April 1924, 4.2 million tons of coal were exported from the South Wales ports but in June of that year only 3.4 million tons were exported and by August there were 30,000 miners unemployed in South Wales with 35 pits closed down. Coal exports continued to fall, bringing tremendous hardship to the people of the valleys. In the whole of 1938 only 10.8 million tons of coal were exported, and this figure dropped even further to just 1.2 million tons in 1947. By 1980 only 4 per cent of the area's coal production was for export.

Bad times had certainly hit the Coalfield. In 1921, 271,161 miners had produced over 46 million tons of coal, 20.1 per cent of the UK's total, but by 1939 there were only 128,774 men at work producing some 35 million tons of coal, 15.2 per cent of the total UK output. In 1931 unemployment within the Coalfield stood at 36 per cent, rising to an incredible 47 per cent in 1932, and in the years 1933, 1934 and 1935 the figures remained devastatingly high at 42, 44 and 34 per cent respectively. Indeed they could have been much higher except for the relative prosperity of the anthracite section of the Coalfield, and for the workmen who chose to leave the area to seek work elsewhere – almost 22,000 men in the period 1931 to 1935. The Rhondda/Port Talbot registration area was particularly badly hit during this period with unemployment peaking at 60 per cent in 1932.

In 1945 the newly elected Labour government introduced the Coal Industry Nationalisation Bill to Parliament, which became law in 1946. Alongside this a Ministry of Fuel and Power survey in 1946 declared that there were 200 years of workable coal reserves left in South Wales. On 1 January 1947 a public corporation called the National Coal Board (NCB) was set up to run the coal industry and to be responsible for that industry on behalf of the people through Parliament. Its task was to bring about the efficient development of the nation's coal production and to develop the industry with the best possible advantage to the public. It was envisaged from the outset that it should pay its own way.

The NCB immediately became the largest employer of labour in the country with a workforce of 800,000. South Wales became one of nine divisions under the title of No. 7, South Western Division and was subdivided into six areas: No. 1 Swansea, No. 2 Maesteg, No. 3 Rhondda, No. 4 Aberdare, No. 5 Rhymney, No. 6 Monmouthshire and Severn (Forest of Dean, Somerset, Bristol). The Division consisted of 220 collieries and over 100 small privately owned mines. The Monmouthshire Area was to be the largest employer with 23,707 men on its books, followed by the Swansea Area with 17,500. The Rhondda Area employed 13,142 men and the Aberdare Area 7,550. In the early 1940s there had been a great demand for coal and many pits had been kept open although operating at a loss, and while this high level of demand continued after nationalisation the NCB embarked on a policy of distributing the finances that were available to the pits which they believed offered the best returns. Within two years of taking over they had closed twenty pits in the Division, including the Pembrokeshire part of the Coalfield where the last pit, Hook's West Park, was closed in 1948, and in the period from 1947 to 1959 a total of 76 collieries were to close. Alongside the closures the NCB started to invest heavily in new ventures, redeveloping at Mardy and Fernhill in the Rhondda and at Llanharan and Nantgarw near the southern outcrop. The exception was in the anthracite area, as although the NCB had invested a million pounds in this part of the Coalfield in 1947 it was disappointed by its returns; the markets for anthracite coals were shrinking, productivity was low, the mines were hopelessly outdated and most went too far into the seams to be economically worked. They claimed that the anthracite miners were reluctant to embrace new mining methods and to abandon their old practices, and at times were downright obstructive. The financial losses of the anthracite pits were far worse than any other part of the United Kingdom and they seemed doomed for extinction. That is until the Clean Air Act of the mid-1950s, after which suddenly anthracite coals were in great demand for central heating systems. The result was a great reversal in the fortunes of the area. New drift mines were opened, and two new super-pits, Cynheidre and Abernant, were sunk, the latter becoming the deepest pit in the Coalfield at 897 yards (820 metres).

The 1950s continued to see a decline in the industry, partly due to the closure of uneconomic collieries and partly due to the miners 'voting with their feet' and seeking healthier, safer and better-paid jobs, in factories and elsewhere. This decline is best illustrated by the following figures.

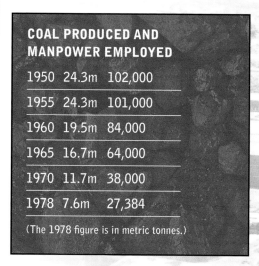

| COAL PRODUCED AND MANPOWER EMPLOYED | | |
|---|---|---|
| 1950 | 24.3m | 102,000 |
| 1955 | 24.3m | 101,000 |
| 1960 | 19.5m | 84,000 |
| 1965 | 16.7m | 64,000 |
| 1970 | 11.7m | 38,000 |
| 1978 | 7.6m | 27,384 |

(The 1978 figure is in metric tonnes.)

The relative wages of the miners were also losing ground. In 1952 the South Wales miner earned £1.92 per shift as compared to £2.08 on average for the UK, but although by 1959 the South Wales average had increased to £2.78 the UK average had climbed to £3.02.

In 1960, in Monmouthshire there were 24 pits in operation employing 16,640 men; by the end of that decade nine pits were left employing just 3,943 men. By 1970 there were only three pits left in the Rhondda Valleys; Fernhill at the top of the Rhondda Fawr, Mardy at the top of the Rhondda Fach and Lewis Merthyr/Ty Mawr at the mouth of the valley.

This mass closure policy had the desired effect of improving the output per manshift at collieries; it went up from just over one ton in 1960 to 1.4 tons in 1970, but it failed to stem the huge losses that the Division was running up. From the position of showing a small profit of £1 per ton in 1950, by 1960 the Division was showing a loss of £28 per ton and by 1970, despite all the closures, losses were running at £41 per ton. The simple fact was that during the 1960s the main customers for coal were turning to other, cheaper sources for their energy, mainly oil.

The election of a Conservative government under the leadership of Margaret Thatcher in 1979 marked the beginning of the end for the Coalfield. In 1978 manpower stood at 27,384, but by the end of the miner's strike in 1985 it had been halved to 13,500 and by 1995 British Coal (the successor to the National Coal Board) had ceased to exist. Between 1979 and 1982 five pits closed, followed by another five in 1983, and in the wake of the defeat of the miners in the 1984–85 strike twelve were closed in 1985, one in 1986, two in 1989, two in 1990, four in 1991, two in 1992 and the last one, Tower, in 1994.

# SECTION 1

Section 1 covers five valleys - Gwendraeth Valley, Amman Valley, Swansea (Tawe) Valley, Dulais Valley and the Vale of Neath, in an area just north of Llanelli and eastwards to Glynneath. The following pages feature a brief history of each pit and a selection of photographs, mainly from the National Museum of Wales, John Cornwell collection with some additional images from other sources.

1/1a **Cynheidre** – Five Roads

2   **Llanelli, Betws** – Ammanford

3   **Abernant** – Pontardawe

4   **Blaenant** – Crynant

5   **Aberpergwm** – Glynneath

# THE GWENDRAETH VALLEY

The Gwendraeth Valley forms the western extremity of the South Wales Coalfield. The coals to be found beneath its surface are prime anthracite coals, and form part of the anthracite coal beds of South Wales, which is the only place in the UK where anthracite is found apart from a small deposit in Scotland. It is a broad, straight valley populated by small settlements, unlike the heavily populated valleys of the steam-coal areas. To the north it extends to just beyond Cross Hands, while to the south Llanelli is just outside the anthracite area. The coal beds were accumulated between 315 and 290 million years ago with the main productive group of coal seams being in the Middle and Lower Coal Measures. Coal mining in the Gwendraeth Valley consisted of driving slants down from the outcrops of the coal seams and following the seams down deeper until eventually the long distances travelled caused ventilation and haulage problems, making the pits uneconomic. When the NCB took control of the nation's mines in 1947 they found that the anthracite collieries were sustaining the worst financial losses in the whole of the UK. The NCB's solution was to gradually close all the old slants and concentrate coal production in two 'super-pits', Abernant Colliery in the Swansea Valley and Cynheidre Colliery in the Gwendraeth Valley, plus a few modern slants such as Cwmgwili. However, these deeper mines failed to reach the expected outputs and were closed in the late 1980s, leaving opencast as the last vestige of mining in the Gwendraeth Valley.

Cynheidre Colliery from the railway sidings in 1989, showing the two 150 feet Koepe Towers which were both downcast ventilation shafts
**Image courtesy Gareth Roden**

# CYNHEIDRE COLLIERY | CLOSED 1989

Ordnance Survey grid references/postcodes:
> SN 526106 / SA15 5LW
> SN 491074 / SA15 5YF

Operating dates: **1953–1989**

Depth: No. 1 Pit: 2,395 feet
> No. 2 Pit: 2,360 feet
> No. 3 Pit: 2,281 feet
> No. 4 Pit: 2,100 feet

Seams worked: **Big Vein** and **Pumpquart**

Owners: National Coal Board, British Coal

Maximum manpower/output:
**1974 – 1,100 men / 320,000 tonnes**

It was in 1951 that the National Coal Board announced that it had agreed to finance the sinking of a new pit in the Gwendraeth Valley. The new colliery was to be located five miles to the north of Llanelli and was intended to be the largest of its kind in the UK, costing £7.5 million. It was planned to work seven seams of prime anthracite coal starting in 1956. All this was based on boreholes proving that the Big Vein was found to be lying at a depth of 2,550 feet. In their characteristically optimistic forecasts, the NCB envisaged output at a million tons per year from 1962 with 3,450 men employed.

Surface work for this colliery started in 1953. The NCB asked the National Union of Mineworkers (NUM) if they could employ a German firm for the sinking of the shafts as they had great difficulty in finding a British firm that could do the work. At the time it was the most expensive undertaking by the NCB anywhere in the UK. The Nos. 1 & 2 shafts were sunk about four miles north of Llanelli between 1954 and 1956 to form a new super-pit incorporating Pentremawr and Great Mountain collieries. It was to exploit 196 square miles of virgin, deep-lying prime anthracite seams. It was estimated that there were ten million tonnes of coal in that area. The No. 1 shaft was 24 feet in diameter while the No. 2 shaft was 20 feet.

Three shafts were sunk while an existing fourth one was extended in order to mine anthracite at depth. The sinking of the No. 1 shaft began in March 1954 and was completed in August 1956. The No. 2 shaft commenced in April 1954 and was completed in September 1956. Shaft No. 3 (formerly Great Mountain No. 3 shaft) was sunk between 1939 and 1941 and deepened in 1955. Shaft No. 4, an additional ventilation shaft, was sunk adjacent to shaft No. 3 and completed in 1964. Shafts 3 and 4 were situated near the village of Pontyberem, some three and a half miles away from Nos. 1 and 2. These four shafts provided the ventilation to the entire underground system. Shafts 1 and 4, the downcast shafts, provide fresh air to all the underground workings while Nos. 2 and 3, the upcast shafts, were fitted with ventilation fans to draw the air through the workings and expel any foul air into the atmosphere.

To complete the ventilation system, a series of underground roadways was driven to connect shafts 3 and 4. Two horizontal drivages at depths of 560 and 660 yards connected the two collieries. These horizontal roadways are known as laterals and at planned points along the laterals further roadways were driven at 90 degrees off the laterals. These roadways, known as cross measures, cross the strata until the coal seam is reached.

The men at this colliery came under criticism from both the NUM and the NCB in 1968 over their high rate of absenteeism, which was called 'shocking'. A five-week-long joint NCB/NUM investigation could find no reason for the levels of absence from work.

By August 1973 absenteeism had reached 30 per cent and the NCB warned that the pit could shut if the absence rate did not improve.

In 1986 British Coal announced that they intended to invest £30 million at Cynheidre Colliery and the proposed Carway Fawr Drift, work on which which was started in 1986, but along with Cynheidre Colliery it closed in January 1989.

The colliery employed 1,043 men on closure, at which time there was an estimated 40 miles of underground roadways in use, while 600-horsepower pumps were removing 10 to 15 million gallons of water a week from the mine.

An outburst of coal and gas in the BV20 District on Tuesday 3/9/74 whilst opening the coalface

From the coalface the coal arrived at the tram loading point. It was loaded into one tonne mine cars for the journey to pit bottom

At pit bottom the mine cars were loaded onto the carriage for transportation to the surface

Cynheidre had the rare privilege for a South Wales mine, in that it had enough room for a spacious surface set-up

Valerie Ganz and her captivating smile at Cynheidre in 1983. Valerie was born in Swansea and studied painting, sculpture and stained glass in the local art college. She remained as a teacher until 1973 when the call of her vocation led her to painting full time, including spending several days and weeks underground at local collieries. Sadly, this well-acclaimed artist died in 2015, aged 79 years. She has exhibited at the famous Glynn Vivian Gallery in Swansea with 14 of her paintings being held in public collections in Wales and England

This photograph shows the three tramroads near pit bottom with the full mine cars waiting to be sent up the pit

# AMMAN VALLEY

The Amman Valley starts its short journey up in the Black Mountains, and then makes its way to Pantyffynnon where it joins the River Loughor. Along this journey it passes through the northernmost reaches of the South Wales Coalfield and its prime anthracite coals. There is little difficulty in identifying the villages of the Amman Valley: Pontamman, Glanamman, Brynamman, Rhosamman and the main settlement, Ammanford. Although there are a few odd ones such as Gwaun-cae-Gurwen! From small beginnings at Brynlloi in 1757 the coal industry grew rapidly once communications were made with the coast. In all, over 120 mines were worked in this area; by the time of nationalisation in 1947 this figure had been whittled down to ten. The Jubilee and Ammanford Top Slant closed in 1947 and Glanamman in 1948. There was then a brief respite until the mid-1950s when Saron closed. The 1960s saw the end of the Gwaun-cae-Gurwen pits when the East Pit closed in 1962; Cwmgorse said goodbye in 1964, Wernos in 1965 and Pantyffynnon in 1969. This left Ammanford Colliery, which was replaced in the 1970s by Betws, the last NCB mine to work in West Wales. failed to reach the expected outputs and were closed in the late 1980s, leaving opencast as the last vestige of mining in the Gwendraeth Valley.

A coalface machine operator wearing a dust extracting helmet - the dust from anthracite coals created major health problems at an earlier age than other coals

# BETWS NEW MINE | CLOSED 2003

Ordnance Survey grid reference/postcode:
SN 644120 / SA18 2FF

Operating dates: **1974–2003**

Seams worked: **Red Vein**

Owners: National Coal Board,
Betws Anthracite Ltd

Maximum manpower/output:
**1979 – 569 men / 385,000 tonnes**

Coal started to come off the conveyor belts in 1974 after the mine was officially opened by Prince Charles on 1 March. There was one embarrassing moment, as one of the Welsh signs had been spelt wrongly and only the Prince spotted it. It was the first completely new mine in the South Wales Coalfield for ten years. Considerable emphasis was placed on ensuring good environmental surface features by detailed design on all surface buildings and the provision of adequate screening around the mine.

Two slants were driven into the Red Vein for a distance of 2½ miles with full production starting on the retreat mining method in the spring of 1978. The coalfaces had ultra-sophisticated semi-automatic face control systems and nucleonic steered power loaders. It was the most advanced colliery in Western Europe. In1980 Betws received the Premier Business and Industry Award in recognition of human and social responsibility and environmental quality. From the manpower of 770 men in 1986 it was producing around 12,000 tonnes (the NCB adopted the metric tonne in the mid-1970s) of coal weekly, which gave an overall output per manshift of 3.5 tonnes, and there were 690 men producing 490,000 tonnes of coal in 1988. Betws New Mine employed only 150 men when it was closed by British Coal in January 1993. In 1993 the government offered to tender a licence to work the coal at Betws, a management buyout was successful, and a new company called Betws Anthracite Limited was formed to work it.

The business plan for the Betws management buyout in 1994 had only been for ten years' mining, and on Friday 1 August 2003 that plan ran its final course when the pit was closed, this time for good.

The prime minister visits Betws in July 1976. Left to right; John John Morris, Secretary of State for Wales, Deputy Director South Wales Area; James Callaghan, Prime Minister; Phillip Weekes, Area Director and Roy Barfoot

Work started on the main portal into the new mine in May 1974

Two slants were driven into the Red Vein for a distance of 2½ miles by local contractors James Williams & Co. of Neath

The surface buildings are complete, and the mine is in full production. The manriding train is going into the mine and coal is coming out

Gullick-Dobson self-advancing roof supports hold up the roof to allow the disc shearer to do its job

# SWANSEA (TAWE) VALLEY

The coal seams of this valley varied tremendously in type, value and thickness. To the south of Pontardawe the seams produced good steam and manufacturing coals, while to the north of Pontardawe they were anthracite in nature. The Graigola seam was particularly valued, with its strong roof needing little support. It also produced only a small amount of ash and had an average thickness of 40 inches. The straight, trenchlike valley from Clydach to Ystradgynlais is eroded along a major disturbance in the coal measures and as a result most of the mines in this valley were levels or slants driven into the mountainsides where the coal seams outcropped. The only two deep mines in the area, Cefn Coed to the east and Abernant Colliery, encountered very difficult conditions.

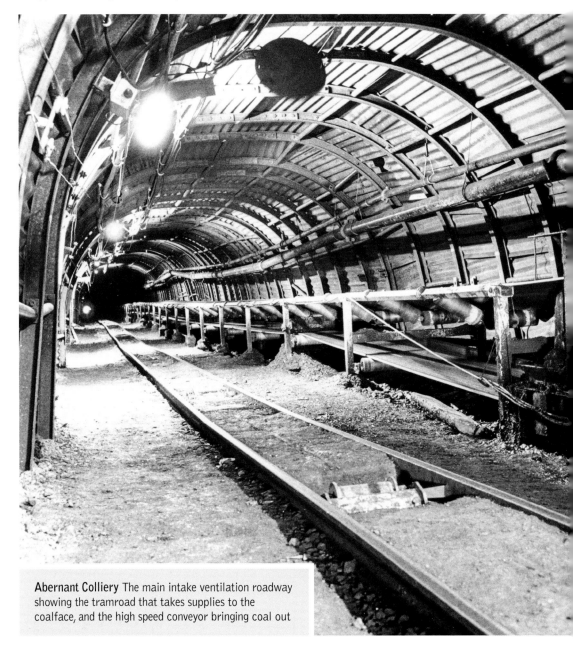

**Abernant Colliery** The main intake ventilation roadway showing the tramroad that takes supplies to the coalface, and the high speed conveyor bringing coal out

Location: **Cwmgorse**

Ordnance Survey grid reference/postcode:
SN 701082 / SA8 4SY

Operating dates: **1953–1988**

Depth: North Pit: 2,961 feet
       South Pit: 2,510 feet

Seams worked: **Peacock, Red Vein**

Owners: National Coal Board, British Coal

Maximum manpower/output:
**1972 – 1,007 men / 365,000 tons**

The sinkings at Abernant commenced in 1953 approximately four miles to the north of Pontardawe and 3½ miles from the northern outcrop of the Coalfield. It was in a broad valley with over two miles of open countryside. The working area was five miles both to the north/south and on the east/west axis. In sinking this mine it was hoped to recapture the one million tons plus annual trade with Canada that had been lost during the war. The winding engines were electrically driven, 2,000 horsepower for the south pit and capable of raising and lowering 80 to 100 men 6 to 9 tonnes of coal per wind in two decks which carried three mine cars per deck. The north pit had a 1,500 hp engine. It was intended to man it from the closures of Cwmgorse, West, Steer and Cwmllynfell collieries, eventually providing jobs for 2,000 miners producing 3,000 tons of coal every working day. In 1968 the absence rate at Abernant was 20 per cent, and 118 men from the closed Yniscedwyn pit were transferred to Abernant to cover the shortage in manpower, although some of the Yniscedwyn men refused to work at Abernant due to it having a shaft, whereas they were used to going down a slant and were nervous of a direct drop to the workings. In 1983 the NCB reported that this colliery was losing £16.20 on every tonne of coal it produced. The total manpower at that time was 835 men. Abernant ceased mining coal in 1988 but the washery stayed open until 1992, receiving trainloads of coal from Betws Drift Mine at Ammanford.

Mine cars near the pit bottom - the South pit winding engines were electrically driven by 2,000 horsepower motors and were capable of raising and lowering 80 - 100 men per wind, or 6 - 9 tonnes of coal per wind in two decks which carried three mine cars per deck

Another view near the pit bottom. By 1980 there were 44 miles of underground roads similar to this, and 10 miles of conveyor belts in the Red Vein

The South pit was started on the 8th January 1954 and the North pit on the 25th January 1954. Sinking was completed in 1958 to a depth of 2,510 feet in the No.1 Pit (North Pit and Upcast), and to a depth of 2,961 feet in the No.2 Pit (South Pit and Downcast). They were the deepest pits in the South Wales Coalfield and were 24 feet in diameter

The destruction of the winding towers at Abernant was carried out on the 10th June 1995

The end of the anthracite Super-Pit

The winding engines are just visible amongst the ruins of the winding shed

# DULAIS VALLEY

The Dulais Valley is an offshoot of the Vale of Neath, and runs for about eight miles from Aberdulais in the south to Onllwyn at the northern end of the valley. Surprisingly the end furthest away from the markets, the north, was the first to be exploited with the opening of the Drim Colliery in 1823. This was followed by the Onllwyn Colliery in 1841 and Banwen Colliery in 1845. There is a fascinating tale behind the name of Seven Sisters, in the middle of the valley. The local coal owner, Evan Bevan, wanted to name his new colliery and village after Isabella, one of his seven daughters. His son intervened on his other sibling's behalf and they were instead named Seven Sisters, although Isabella did cut the first sod for the sinking. Cefn Coed Colliery at the southern end of the valley was the deepest anthracite mine in the world on sinking, and it was on this site that Blaenant Drift became the last mine to be worked in this valley.

The Blaenant Drift was located adjacent to the Cefn Coed Colliery and shared many of its facilities including the upcast shaft for common ventilation

# BLAENANT COLLIERY |

Location: **Near Crynant**

Ordnance Survey grid reference/postcode:
SN 795049 / SA10 8SR

Operating dates: **1935–1990**

Seams worked: **No. 2 Rhondda**

Owners: Blaenant Colliery Co., National Coal Board, British Coal

Maximum manpower/output:
**1978 – 591 men / 451,230 tonnes**

The Blaenant Colliery Company was incorporated in 1930 to work the Blaenant Drift which was driven into the No. 2 Rhondda seam. The colliery came under the control of the National Coal Board in 1947 and was placed in the South Western Division's No. 1 Swansea Area but by 1954 it had been moved to the No. 9 Neath Area, No. 1 Group. A new drift from the surface of Cefn Coed Colliery was completed in 1963, then replaced in 1971 by another surface drift. The new drift shortened the coal routes to the surface of the mine by 6,700 feet. The coalfaces were to be worked by the retreat system and three Dosco Heading machines had to tunnel to just over 4,300 yards until the new faces could be opened. At the surface of the mine a whole train load of 32 wagons (1,000 tonnes of coal) destined for Aberthaw Power Station could be loaded in 25 minutes by the 'merry-go-round' system. Loading, transporting 50 miles and discharging took only three hours.

This colliery was a regular record breaker in a mineral take that was virtually fault free, a phenomenon that is unknown in the rest of the South Wales Coalfield. In 1978 it was the first mine in South Wales to be equipped with three coal cutters on a 650-foot coalface. Production then increased from 3,000 tons to 5,000 tons per week from this face. In 1988, 590 men produced 500,000 tonnes of coal. In April 1990 British Coal stated that output at Blaenant was below half of what was expected and, because of the geology, there was no hope of hitting the target of 15,000 tonnes a week. It was said that the mine had lost money in the past year, so it was closed by British Coal on the 11 May 1990. On closure it had ten miles of underground roadways and three miles of conveyor belts.

The surface drift was 700 yards long, 16 feet wide and driven down at a gradient of 1 in 3.7

Cen Coed was the deepest anthracite mine in the world when sunk, going down 2254 feet. It closed in April 1968

Only the one coal seam, the No.2 Rhondda, was worked at Blaenant, at the time of the photograph (late 1970s) the coalface length was up to 200 metres with an average advance of 2.43m per day on a double coaling shift system

The afternoon shift waiting to go down in 1977

The entrance to Cefn Coed Museum which opened in 1986 - well worth a visit if you are down that way
**The Author**

A commemorative plate manufactured in 1990 showing a flame safety lamp in the centre and twelve local mines around the rim. On the back is a brief description of Blaenant Colliery

# VALE OF NEATH

The development of industry at the top end of the Vale of Neath could only take place with improved communications to the Bristol Channel, and from there on to the various markets that were now demanding more and more Welsh coal as the Industrial Revolution spread beyond home shores.

The first Act of Parliament for the construction of the Neath Canal was obtained in 1791, and the canal itself was completed to Giant's Grave in 1798. The canal was fourteen miles long and cost £40,000 to complete. To link the canal to the various works and mines that started to flourish in the valley, tramroads were constructed along its length with the longest being from the top end of the canal and all the way up to Hirwaun. The coal mined in the Cwmgwrach area was connected to the main canal by an offshoot canal called Cnel Bach.

Due to a geological disturbance called the Neath Trough the Vale of Neath can be a very difficult area to mine, as, starting with a Mr Protheroe who had come all the way from Bristol, the many owners of Cwmgwrach, Blaengwrach and Aberpergwm found out. Even the huge resources of the National Coal Board failed to get the returns that they believed lay hidden 'under them thar hills' and they gave up the struggle in 1983.

That didn't stop the new wave of mine owners from giving it a go in the vicinity, which only brought about another wave of despair and bankruptcies in places such as Pentreclwydau and Aberpergwm. At the time of writing in 2018 the last large mining concerns in this area, Aberpergwm and Unity, are just ticking over, hoping for better days to come.

The Pentreclwydau drift was opened by the National Coal Board to exploit the western take of Aberpergwm Colliery. It was closed in May 1967. Two drifts from Aberpergwm had previously tried to work this area in 1940 but ventilation and haulage problems forced them to pull out

# ABERPERGWM COLLIERY

Location: **Glynneath**

Ordnance Survey grid reference/postcode: SN 864059 / SA11 5RF

Operating dates: **1863–2010**

Seams worked: **Eighteen-Feet, Nine-Feet, White-Four-Feet, Three-Feet, Cornish and Peacock seams**

Owners: Aberpergwm Colliery Company, G.H. Williams, Aberpergwm Collieries Ltd., Vale of Neath Colliery Co., Amalgamated Anthracite Collieries Co., National Coal Board, British Coal, Glo Tech, Rhydian, Single Fern, Anthracite Mining Limited, Walter Energy

Maximum manpower/output: **1955 – 703 men / 143,743 tons**

The 'modern' Aberpergwm workings date from 1863 with the associated Pwllfaron Slant reopened in 1906. It was worked by the Aberpergwm Colliery Company in the Nine-Feet, Three-Feet and Cornish seams. Following nationalisation in 1947, Aberpergwm was placed in the NCB's South Western Division's Area No. 9 (Neath), Group No. 1. At that time the slant was working the Eighteen-Feet, Nine-Feet, White-Four-Feet and Peacock anthracite seams using the heading-and-stall system of extraction. In the late 1950s the NCB reorganised the mines in the Glynneath area, opening new slants at Cwmgwrach and Pentreclwydau, and constructed a new central washery at Aberpergwm. In 1983 the Coal Board reported that this colliery was losing £44.70 for each tonne of coal produced, the second worst figures in the Coalfield. Following the year-long miners' strike the colliery made a poor recovery, and by 22 April 1985 had achieved only 45 per cent of expected targets. Under pressure from the NCB a mass meeting of the men agreed to the closure of the colliery, which was carried out on 7 October 1985. It was later reopened under private ownership, when it took a year to pump the water out of the mine and new 984-feet-long drifts were also driven. It has had several owners since including Glo Tech, Rhydian, Single Fern and Anthracite Mining Limited. In 2000 the government gave the owners of this mine grants totalling a million pounds, and in March of 2003 it again qualified for £903,600 in the final part of the Coal Operating Aid Scheme. In 2010 its Canadian owners reported that the future was 'rosy' for Aberpergwm but by 2012 the realities of the marketplace had brought about the 'suspension' of work at Aberpergwm by Walter Energy.

The washery with the drift in the background during demolition

The Dosco Roadhead Dinter was used to drive headings, the rotating head would rip down the coal/stone from the face, gathering arms at the front of the machine would then scoop it up and dump it onto a conveyor behind the machine

The bridge over the River Neath that linked the Blaengwrach mine with the Aberpergwm washery. This washery could handle 250 tons of coal per hour from Aberpergwm, Pentreclwydau, Blaengwrach and Rhigos collieries

general view of the pithead baths and bus/car park - date unknown

# SECTION 2

Section 2 covers five valleys - Afan Valley, Llynfi Valley, Garw Valley, Ogmore Valleys and Ely Valley in an area from Glyncorrwg over to the east and just south of Pontypridd. The following pages feature a brief history of each pit and a selection of photographs, mainly from the National Museum of Wales, John Cornwell collection with some additional images from other sources.

1 **Glyncorrwg** – Glyncorrwg

2 **St. John's** – Maesteg

3 **Garw** – Blaengarw & Ffaldau – Pontycymmer

4 **Wyndham** – Pricetown & Western – Nantymoel

5 **Cwm** – Beddau

# AFAN VALLEY

Mining came relatively late to the Upper Afan Valley, and started generally with the opening of the South Wales Mineral Railway in the 1860s which enabled coal to be extracted on a large scale. Glyncorrwg pit quickly became a booming business, followed by Cymmer in the 1870s, Dyffryn in 1890, and Abergwynfi and Blaengwynfi in 1892/93. Between 1861 and 1901 the population of the parish of Glyncorrwg grew tenfold, from roughly 600 people to well over 6,000. This period didn't last long and by the 1920s the picture in the Afan Valley was one of sheer deprivation. During the 1921 lock-out, some 5,000 men were thrown out of work, with the same happening again in 1926. The area wasn't passive by any means and acts of defiance in the form of riots became regular occurrences.

On nationalisation in 1947 the Afan Valley collieries were placed in the No. 2. Maesteg Area and consisted of Avon, Nantewlaith, Glyncorrwg, North Rhondda, Garth Tonmawr and Duffryn Rhondda, although North Rhondda No. 2 closed almost immediately and Nantewlaith in 1948. The massive mines closure programme of the 1960s finished off most of the others with Garth Tonmawr closed in 1964, Duffryn Rhondda 1966, Avon in 1969 and Glyncorrwg in 1970.

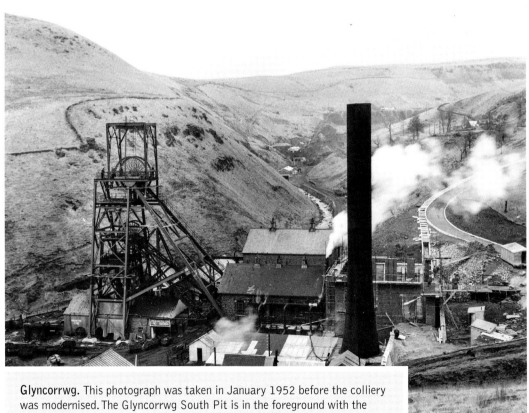

**Glyncorrwg.** This photograph was taken in January 1952 before the colliery was modernised. The Glyncorrwg South Pit is in the foreground with the North Pit behind it. In the background is the north Rhondda Colliery

Location: **Glyncorrwg**

Ordnance Survey grid reference/postcode:
SN 887001 / SA13 3AY

Operating dates: **1904–1970**

Depth: **1,283 feet**

Seams worked: **No. 2 Rhondda, Red, Six-Feet, Nine-Feet, Peacock**

Owners: Glyncorrwg Colliery Co., Amalgamated Anthracite Collieries Ltd, National Coal Board

Maximum manpower/output:
**1954 – 772 men / 156,217 tons**

On nationalisation in 1947 the colliery was placed in the NCB South Western Division's No. 2 Area, Afan Group. On 13 January 1954 there was an explosion that injured around twenty miners, and the district had to be sealed off permanently to prevent the fires from spreading. At around 9.30am a collier hit a steel wedge with a sledgehammer, creating a spark that caused an explosion of methane gas out of which a flame shot along the coalface. Of the thirty-two colliers working on the coalface, seventeen received severe burns, seven were slightly burned and eight were untouched. A rescue party put out all the clothing that was on fire but when they reached the No. 7 stent they were forced back by the intense heat. Just before noon the roof collapsed in this area, releasing more gas, and flames started to burn along the coalface. It was then decided to pull out of the district and seal it off to prevent fresh air from entering and prolonging the fires.

Glyncorrwg Colliery was working the anthracite Six-Feet Seam and from this seam the methane gas was extracted and, along with the gas from Duffryn Rhondda and Avon collieries, was sent to the gasworks at Aberavon and used to service 45,000 homes. Glyncorrwg Colliery was closed on 1 May 1970 on the dual grounds that it was uneconomic and its coal was unmarketable.

A row of, what is thought to be, sinkers cottages near the colliery. On the 30th of September 1891 eight of the shaft sinkers were killed in the South Pit when the book that they were in overwound

Just above Glyncorrwg were the North Rhondda Levels. Opened in 1908 they worked the No.2 Rhondda seam until they closed in 1960

The new washery after re-construction, features a 250 ton per hour heavy density washer

New surface buildings were provided as well as new sidings to hold 184 full and 215 empty 12 ton wagons

# GARW VALLEY

In the Garw Valley most of the coal-mining activity was crammed into the top 2½ miles between Blaengarw and Pontycymmer. Prior to the 1800s there were only a few small levels that had burrowed into the hillsides, then the Ffaldau Colliery was sunk in 1865, followed by the likes of International, Garw, Lluest and Braich-y-cymmer. By 1913 there were 2,195 miners living in Blaengarw and 1,415 living in Pontycymmer.

The 1920s and 1930s were a period of very hard times for this valley, with closures and short-time work reducing the number of miners to 2,091 in 1947. At nationalisation in 1947 the valley's mines were placed in the NCB South Western Division's No. 2 Maesteg Area.

Glengarw closed in 1959, International in 1967, Ffaldau was merged with Garw in 1975, and Garw Colliery, the last mine in this valley, closed in 1985.

Garw Colliery was located right at the top of the Garw Valley at Blaengarw which can be seen behind the colliery

# GARW/FFALDAU COLLIERY

**Location: Blaengarw** and **Pontycymmer**

Ordnance Survey grid references/postcodes:
SS 905931 / CF32 8AE
SS 903915/ CF32 8NW

Operating dates: **1883–1985 and 1878–1985**

Depth: **1,201 feet and 995 feet**

Seams worked: **Gellideg, Lower Nine-Feet, Bute, Lower Six-Feet, Two-Feet-Nine, Caedavid, Lower Seven-Feet, Middle Seven-Feet, Yard, Red, No. 2 Rhondda.**

Owners: Blaengarw Ocean Coal Co., Ocean Coal Co., Ffaldau Steam Coal Co., Powell Duffryn, National Coal Board

At Garw Colliery the first coal was wound in 1886, and a subsidiary company called the Blaengarw Ocean Coal Company was formed to run the pit. In October 1929 the South Wales Miners' Federation (SWMF) men at the pit went out on strike for three weeks over non-union labour. This strike was unique in that it was the first time that the SWMF had paid their members the equivalent of 'dole' money while they were on strike. In 1930 Garw Colliery lay idle for 105 days, and in 1931 for 119 days, in both cases due to lack of orders. The National Coal Board merged Ffaldau Colliery with the neighbouring Garw (Ocean) Colliery in April 1975, with Ffaldau's coal being diverted underground to the Garw shafts. It was then estimated that the combine had 7.5 million tonnes of coal reserves. Garw/Ffaldau Colliery was closed in 1985.

Ffaldau Colliery was sunk in 1878 by the Ffaldau Steam Coal Company Limited to produce house and steam coals. The downcast ventilation pit was sunk to just below the Lower-Six-Feet Seam to a depth of 663 feet 7 inches, while the upcast ventilation pit was sunk to just below the Upper-Five-Feet Seam to a depth of 995 feet.

In November 1948 the men at this pit gave the NCB a fortnight's notice that they intended to strike due to their wives complaining that there was too much small in the house coal (only lump coal was used on domestic fires). A report in the May 1953 edition of the Coal News stated that there were nine brothers working at this pit: Aneurin, Lee, Phillip, Trevor, Verdun, John, Oliver, Glyndwr and Ninian Stewart; another brother, Gwyn, worked at International Colliery.

Surface craftsmen (and their dogs) gathered in front of the wooden headgear at Garw Colliery c1900
**Amgueddfa Cymru - National Museum Wales**

The Ffaldau Colliery was roughly 1 mile to the south of the Garw Pit and located in the centre of Pontycymmer

Ffaldau Colliery in the days of steam winders. In 1950/2 there was a revamp which resulted in output increasing from 580 tons a day in 1949 to 920 tons a day in 1950
**Amgueddfa Cymru - National Museum Wales**

Garw Colliery today; once, over 900 men laughed, cried and toiled together under this field
**The Author**

# LLYNFI VALLEY

The Llynfi Valley's first major contact with industry was in 1780 when a blast furnace was established at Cefn Cribbwr. This was followed by the works of the Maesteg Iron Company in 1826, which together with its associated coal and iron mines trebled the population of Maesteg by 1831. In all, around fifty coal mines of various sizes worked in this valley until the last one, St John's, closed in 1985. Today there is little left to remind us of its industrial past even though it was heavily mined, both for the deep steam coals and for house and manufacturing coals from levels into the upper coal series.

A lamproom attendant checking that the batteries are positioned correctly for charging

# ST. JOHN'S COLLIERY | CLOSED 1985

Location: **Maesteg**

Ordnance Survey grid reference/postcode:
SS 876917 / CF34 0DH

Operating dates: **1910–1985**

Depth: **1,263 feet**

Seams worked: **Gellideg, Five-Feet, Yard, Bute, Harvey, Lower-Six-Feet, Upper-Six-Feet, Two-Feet-Nine, Victoria, Seven-Feet**

Owners: North's Navigation Collieries Ltd, Welsh Associated Collieries Ltd, Powell Duffryn Associated Collieries Ltd, National Coal Board

Maximum manpower/output:
**1961 – 843 men / 345,248 tons**

On nationalisation of the UK's coal mines in January 1947, St John's Colliery was placed in the National Coal Board South Western Division's Area No. 2, Maesteg Group, and at that time employed 185 men on the surface and 976 men underground working the Six-Feet, Lower and Upper Five-Feet, Two-Feet-Nine and New seams. By 1980 this pit had around 13 miles of underground roadways in use and around five miles of conveyor belts at work, which was one of the reasons for losses which were running at £37,000 per week. A plan to alleviate the transportation delays involved driving a new one-mile roadway from the pit bottom to the current workings. In 1981 the manager complained to his superiors that he needed a hundred more men if he was to complete the development programme. At this time the NCB was investing heavily in this pit to reach an estimated 20 million tonnes of coal reserves, and it also bored down in eleven different places in an attempt to prove new areas. It all came to nothing, however. In 1983 the colliery was losing £40.20 for every tonne of coal that it produced, the third worst figures in the South Wales Coalfield. In April 1985, the Coal Board said that the pit had become impossible to work successfully as a result of hopeless geology and because productivity had slumped to the lowest rate in the Coalfield. On 7 May 1985 the NCB's Area Director visited the pit and announced that redundancies would begin immediately. The NUM Lodge agreed to a reduction of around 300 men to a total of 350 but opposed closure and was the first to apply to the Modified Review Procedure. However, this was to no avail and the colliery closed in November 1985.

On Friday the 24th of May 1974 Prince Charles made an underground visit to the S1 District

A good aerial view of the colliery, with the pithead baths and medical centre (opened in 1955) at the top left of the photograph

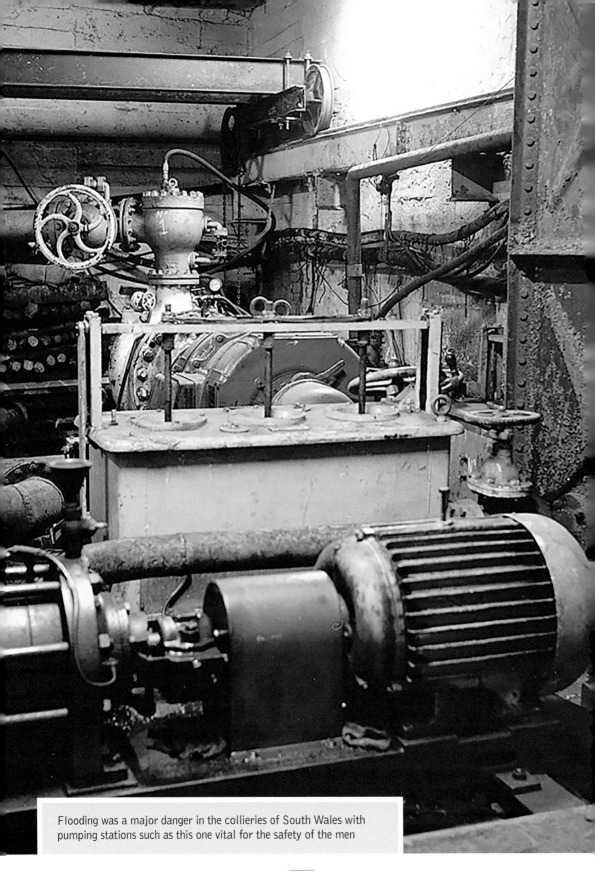

Flooding was a major danger in the collieries of South Wales with pumping stations such as this one vital for the safety of the men

A view of the colliery from the sidings - the untreated coal was taken to the Maesteg Central Washery for cleaning

# OGMORE (OGWR) VALLEYS

Two Ogmore rivers, the Fach and the Fawr, and their associated valleys rise from the hinterland adjoining the Rhondda Fawr Valley and travel the short distance to the Vale of Glamorgan. The Ogmore Fawr Valley has four main settlements – Nantymoel, Ogmore Vale, Price Town and Wyndham – which were constructed in the 1860s to house the workers of the thirteen mines of the area and their families. There are currently about 8,000 people in the area. Located up at the top of the valley, the Wyndham/Western Combine was the last to fly the flag of coal production in this valley.

An abandoned Llewellyn & Cubit steam haulage. Steam was generated in boilers at the surface of the mine and then piped down the shaft to the haulages

# WYNDHAM/WESTERN COLLIERY

Location: **Price Town, Nantymoel**

Ordnance Survey grid references/postcodes:
**SS 933920 / CF32 7PN**
**SS 938926 / CF32 7NJ**

Operating dates: **1865–1984 and 1873–1984**

Depth: Wyndham: **1,427 feet**
      Western: **1,562 feet**

Seams worked: **Lower Six-Feet, Five-Feet, Phils, Brunts, Middle Seven-Feet, Yard, Lower Nine-Feet, Caerau, Gellideg, Seven-Feet, Nine-Feet, A seam, D seam**

Maximum manpower/output:
**1971\* – 1,188 men / 475,000 tons**
\*Maximum figures under NCB control

At Western two shafts were sunk about ten miles to the north of Bridgend and 400 yards to the south-east of Nantymoel Church, and on the site of the old Blaenogwr Colliery. They were 50 yards apart and cost £65,676 to sink. On 3 July 1942 the manager of this colliery, J. Jones, was fined £2 plus £3 costs by magistrates for assaulting a surface worker called J. Hughes. Apparently Mr Jones objected to Hughes swearing at him.

Wyndham Colliery was eight miles to the north of Bridgend and was sunk in 1865 by the Llynvi, Tondu and Ogmore Vale Iron and Coal Company. Between 1957 and 1965, at a cost of £3 million, Wyndham Colliery was merged with the neighbouring Western Colliery with the estimated reserves for the combine given as 62 million tons of coal. During the reorganisation the Wyndham downcast shaft was deepened by 120 yards to a depth of 435 yards and the Western upcast shaft deepened to a depth of 476 yards. A 315-yard roadway was driven to connect the pits, which was completed in 1962. Two new winders (600 hp and 1,700 hp) and headgear were installed at Western and a new winder was installed at Wyndham No. 1 Pit. Western Colliery's coal was taken by underground conveyors to a bunker 1,300 yards from the Wyndham pit bottom and from there shunted by one of three 65 hp diesel locomotives.

The NCB announced the closure because of hopeless mining conditions. The 537 miners were offered alternative jobs or redundancy and Wyndham/Western Colliery was closed in January 1984

A general view of the Wyndham pit top - if you look carefully you can see the Western headgear in the distance between the two shafts

Operating the controls of a self-advancing roof support in 1975. The combine employed 1,188 men and produced 475,000 tonnes, the largest output in the Coalfield

The officials of Wyndham Colliery posing for a photograph in 1910 with the headgears as a backdrop
Amgueddfa Cymru - National Museum Wales

The Western Colliery upcast shaft was to a depth of 1140f feet. It was called Edward after the only son of the owner of the Ocean Coal Company. Courtesy David Davies

The Wyndham coal winder was built in the early 1960s with the old engine house on the left behind it, level with the upcast engine house
**Amgueddfa Cymru - National Museum Wales**

# ELY VALLEY

The Ely Valley spills out of the Rhondda Fawr Valley just below Penygraig and Trebanog. The main village, Tonyrefail, was about halfway down the valley. Tonyrefail was the location of Coedely Colliery, while Beddau, which is 1½ miles to the north of Llantrisant, was the home of Cwm Colliery, the last mine to work in this area.

This photograph taken in August 1911 shows the size of the Cwm headgear frame the men standing on it help to illustrate the scale of the structure
Amgueddfa Cymru - National Museum Wales

# CWM/COEDELY COLLIERIES

**Location: Beddau and Tonyrefail**

Ordnance Survey grid references/postcodes:
ST 065864 / CF37 1PU
ST 015861 / CF38 8EX

Operating dates: **1909–1986 and 1901–1985**

Depth: **Cwm shafts: 2,384 feet & 2,099 feet**
**Coedely shafts: 2,604 feet & 2,293 feet**

Seams worked: **Five-Feet, Middle-Five-Feet, Bute, Upper-Nine-Feet, Upper - Four-Feet, No. 3 Rhondda, Six-Feet. Two-Feet-Nine, Lower-Four-Feet, Yard, Lower-Nine-Feet**

Owners: Cwm: Great Western Colliery Co., Powell & Duffryn, NCB

Coedely: Welsh Navigation Steam Coal Co., D. Davies & Sons, NCB

At Cwm the two shafts were named after Lady Mildred and Lady Margaret Bramwell and had the largest pit bottoms in South Wales. It was closed between June 1927 and April 1929 due to lack of trade. Along with the nation's other coal mines both Cwm and Coedely were nationalised in 1947 and placed in the National Coal Board's South Western Division's No. 3 (Rhondda) Area,

which was based at Treorchy. In 1958 Cwm and Coedely were merged to create the largest colliery in the South Wales Coalfield. It was planned to raise 5,500 tons of prime coking coal every day from a reserve estimated at 150 million tons with a projected manpower of 3,000 men. The construction of the massive Coke Works was completed in 1958.

In 1981 another £20 million was invested in this works, which then gave employment to 300 men and produced 325,000 tons of coke. In 1983 Cwm/Coedely Colliery was losing £7.80 for every tonne of coal that it produced and employed 1,274 men. During the 1984/85 miners' strike, Cwm NUM Lodge was one of only five lodges in South Wales to have an injunction placed on them by the working miners. They were also the only NUM Lodge to be prevented by this injunction from picketing at a particular working miner's house. Following the strike, attempts to develop the Six-Feet Seam hit severe geological difficulties and during the first six months of 1986 the pit lost £7 million or a loss of £67 per ton produced. The Coedely section of the mine was closed in April 1985 and the Cwm section on 28 November 1986.

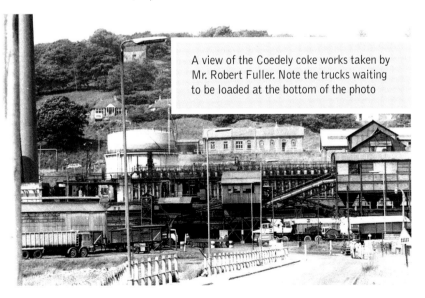

A view of the Coedely coke works taken by Mr. Robert Fuller. Note the trucks waiting to be loaded at the bottom of the photo

A view seldom seen in real life – a nice clean and tidy colliery surface

Unfortunately, the conditions and geology in South Wales created all sorts of problems. In this photograph they had hit faulty ground and needed to re-open the coalface further on

Another view from July 1981 of a heading opening up in faulty ground

The Coedely shafts with the downcast ventilating shaft in the foreground and the upcast shaft behind it

Near the southern outcrop of the Coalfield were found prime coking coals which were processed in plants such as this one at Cwm Colliery

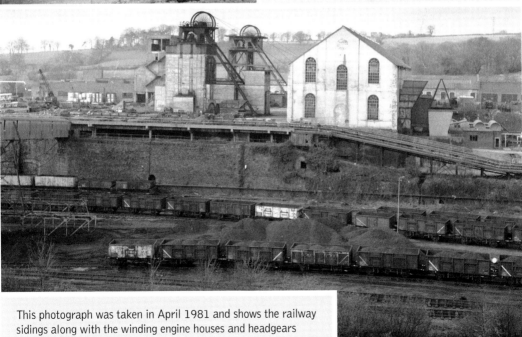

This photograph was taken in April 1981 and shows the railway sidings along with the winding engine houses and headgears

# SECTION 3

Section 3 covers four valleys - Rhondda Valleys, Cynon Valley, Taff Vale and Taff Bargoed Valley in an area from Glyncorrwg over to the east and just south of Pontypridd. The following pages feature a brief history of each pit and a selection of photographs, mainly from the National Museum of Wales, John Cornwell collection with some additional images from other sources.

1 **Mardy** – Maerdy
2 **Lewis Merthyr** – Trehafod
3 **Tower** – Hirwaun
4 **Merthyr Vale** – Aberfan/Merthyr Vale
5 **Taff Merthyr** – Trelewis

# RHONDDA VALLEYS

## Rhondda Fach

Although coal had been mined for local use in the Rhondda Valleys for centuries, it wasn't until the construction of the Glamorganshire Canal in 1798 that this area was laid bare for massive exploitation. In 1809, industrialist Dr Richard Griffiths linked Jeremiah Homfray's level at Hafod Fawr Farm to the canal by means of a tramroad and short canal and made the Rhondda even more accessible. Coal mining in the first part of the nineteenth century remained in this area around the junction of the Rhondda Fawr and Rhondda Fach Valleys until the upper reaches of the valleys were laid open by the Taff Vale Railway in mid-century.

From the tentative steps of Homfray and Walter Coffin, who opened two small levels in 1809, the Rhondda reached an output of 205,200 tons of coal in 1856 and by the end of the century there were 68 working collieries and the Rhondda Valleys had become the most intensively mined area in Great Britain. Coal production peaked at 9.5 million tons in 1913 and by that year there were 53 large pits in the Rhondda with 21 of these employing over 1,000 men underground and 23 employing 500 to 1,000, but six years after the end of the First World War the decline of the coal industry in both the Rhondda and throughout South Wales had commenced.

Following the Great War Germany had to pay reparations particularly to France and Italy thereby cancelling important markets for Rhondda coal. Meanwhile both the Royal Navy and Merchant Navy were turning to oil to fuel their ships, and other nations who were formerly customers were now developing their own fuel resources.

The reduction in the demand for coal for export badly affected the area and this was compounded in 1929 when the general economy of Great Britain collapsed, with the Rhondda Valleys being declared a depressed area. From a peak manpower in the Rhondda pits of 41,416 men in 1911 the number of men employed in 1934 was down to 26,750 (near to the figure of 25,747 men who had been employed in the Rhondda mines in 1891). This figure further dropped to only 19,873 men employed in the Rhondda pits in 1936.

The demand for coal for the nation's factories during World War Two slowed down the decline of the Valley's pits for a while, but by the nationalisation of the coal mines in 1947 there were only twenty-five pits left (with only fifteen of these in production), employing 13,142 men.

The National Coal Board attempted to revitalise the area with massive investments and reorganisations at Mardy and Fernhill but the decline was irreversible and only nine pits were in production by 1960. Mardy Colliery, the last pit to work in the Rhondda Valleys, was closed in 1990.

# MARDY COLLIERY | CLOSED 1990

**Location: Maerdy, Rhondda Fach Valley**

Ordnance Survey grid reference/postcode:
SS 972989 / CF43 4DE

Operating dates: **1875–1990**

Depth: **1,500 feet**

Seams worked: **Abergorchi, Bute, Gorllwyn, Nine-Feet, Six-Feet, Two-Feet-Nine, Four-Feet, Five-Feet, Seven-Feet, Yard**

Owners: Jones & Cobb, Locket's Merthyr Steam Coal Co., Bwllfa & Cwmaman Collieries Ltd, Welsh Associated Collieries Ltd, Powell Duffryn Associated Collieries Ltd, NCB, British Coal

Maximum manpower/output:
**1923 – 3,200 men / 700,000 tons**

On 23 December 1885 an explosion of firedamp killed 81 men and boys at this pit. In 1926 Locket's Merthyr Company went into liquidation and the colliery closed. The pits remained idle during 1927 due to the trading and industrial relations situation. Work resumed on 14 September 1928 when around 100 men were taken on to the books. In 1930 the local miners' lodge was expelled from the SWMF, for being too militant, and remained so until it merged with the new lodge in 1934.

The Nos. 1 and 2 pits were closed in 1932, and work was suspended once more in 1934. Powell Duffryn again closed the colliery for a while, and then reopened it in 1936 on their own terms; by 1938 only 330 men were employed there. No checkweigher was allowed, and no fixed price list for wages was agreed to. Powell Duffryn finally closed the pit in 1940. In 1949 the NCB announced that the first complete colliery redevelopment in the South Wales Coalfield was to be carried out on the site of the Nos. 3 & 4 pits. It was estimated that there were twelve workable seams from the Gorllwyn down to the Gellideg that would yield 120 million tons of coal and give a colliery life of 125 years; they would cover an area of five miles by three. In a £5 million scheme, the surface facilities were completely modernised and the colliery was linked by a 3,200-yard underground roadway to the Bwllfa Dare pit. On 1 April 1986 Mardy's output of coal was diverted by underground roadway to Tower Colliery, and the two mines were merged. Mardy Colliery, the last deep mine to have worked in the Rhondda Valleys, was then closed by British Coal in December 1990. Only seventeen of the 300 men left at the pit opted for a transfer to another mine.

A coalface in 1975. The coalface output per manshift was 4 tonnes, producing 3,000 tonnes of coal a week

A view of the 3 & 4 pits from the other side taken just before closure

The main roadway - taking coal out on the conveyor and supplies in on the tramroad

# LEWIS MERTHYR COLLIERY | CLOSED 1983

Location: **Trehafod, Lower Rhondda Valley**

Ordnance Survey grid reference/postcode:
**ST 039911 / CF37 2NP**

Operating dates: **1850–1983**

Depth: **Coedcae Pit: 115 yards**
**Bertie Pit: 482 yards**

Seams worked: **Lower Five-Feet, Middle Five-Feet, Upper Five-Feet, Two-Feet-Nine, Six-Feet, Red, Nine-Feet, No. 3 Rhondda, Gellideg.**

Owners: Lewis Merthyr Navigation Collieries Ltd, Lewis Merthyr Consolidated Collieries Ltd, Powell Duffryn Steam Coal Company Lid, National Coal Board

Maximum manpower/output:
**1913 – 4,998 men / 1915 – 2 million tons**

This was a complex colliery that consisted of the Coedcae Pits, the Hafod Pits, Lady Lewis Colliery and the Bertie and Trevor Pits. In 1900 W.T. Lewis, later Lord Merthyr of Senghenydd, merged them into the Lewis Merthyr Colliery.

The demand for its coal by the major shipping lines was exceptional and amongst its customers were Cunard, White Star, Pacific & Oriental, Union Castle, Hansa, Anchor, Royal Hungarian and Générale Transatlantique. On 22 November 1956 all the men present in the N4 District were engulfed by flames and suffered severe burns; two died at the scene of the explosion and another seven died later in hospital.

When the NCB announced the closure of this pit in 1983, a ballot of the South Wales Miners then voted by the very narrow margin of 55.4 per cent to strike in support of Lewis Merthyr and to travel to the other coalfields to seek their support. This led to a national ballot on pit closures. In this ballot South Wales increased its vote to almost 65 per cent, and Kent voted 70 per cent for strike action, but elsewhere the call was rejected, even in Yorkshire as well as the more moderate Derby, Leicester and Nottinghamshire coalfields. In all 61 per cent of the miners rejected the strike call, and the South Wales Area of the NUM reluctantly agreed to return to work and allow Lewis Merthyr to close.

A good general view of the colliery taken from the western side

The 'Heavy Gang' on 416s in 1983. As the name implies they transported the bulky and difficult materials around the pit

The bottom of the Bertie Shaft with Benny Roberts on the left of the gates in 1978

The top of the Bertie pit in July 1983, the white shorts were not typical wear at Lewis Merthyr!

Alan Appleby, chocksman, on 416s face
at Lewis Merthyr Colliery in 1983

# CYNON VALLEY

The Cynon Valley was lucky, or perhaps unlucky, to possess the famous Aberdare Four-Feet Seam, whose coal was particularly coveted by the Royal Navy and many other navies of the world. Generally, the lower seams of the valley were classed as Type 201b Dry Steam Coal, which made them the best of their type available in the UK. The lower end of the valley produced Types 202 and 203 Coking Steam Coals, which were still highly desirable. The period between 1840 and 1850 was one of extensive development in the Cynon Valley: the ironworks were still booming, the Industrial Revolution had created a nationwide demand for coal, and the world had discovered the Aberdare Four-Feet seam. Coal speculators laid the valley wide open to exploitation by sinking bigger and deeper pits, and workmen and their families flooded in from all corners of Wales, Ireland and England seeking a better future.

Such was the intensity of mining in the area that by 1860 the Rhondda was overtaking the Cynon Valley as the premier coal-producing region in South Wales, the Cynon was becoming exhausted and many of the coal owners from this valley were turning to the Rhondda for further exploitation. By 1875 the Rhondda's output of coal was greater that the Cynon's, and by 1884 it was double.

On nationalisation of the mines in 1947 the Cynon Valley pits were placed in the National Coal Board's South Western Division, No. 4 Aberdare Area. Only eleven working pits remained, employing 7,550 men, and total output from these pits was about two million tons. In 1961, prior to the National Coal Board's massive closure programme, nine pits were still working in the valley. Aberaman, Cwmaman, Fforchaman and Rhigos were all closed in this period, and mining in Aberdare ceased to exist with only the opencast headquarters remaining at Aberaman. By the time of the next onslaught against the mining industry following the 1984–85 miners' strike only three pits remained, employing 2,542 men. Penrhiwceiber was closed in 1986, Lady Windsor/Abercynon in 1988, and the last British coal mine in the South Wales Coalfield, Tower Colliery, closed in 1994. But that was not the end of Tower's story.

Tower from high up on the mountain road to Treherbert in the Rhondda Fawr Valley. This was taken after the workers buy-out

# TOWER COLLIERY | CLOSED 2008

Location: **Cynon Valley**

Ordnance Survey grid reference/postcode:
**SN 927044 / CF44 9UE**

Operating dates: **1864–2008**

Depth: **Tower No. 4 Pit – 525 feet**

Seams worked: **Five-Feet, Seven-Feet, Nine-Feet, Bute**

Owners: Marquis of Bute, D.R. Lewellyn, Welsh Associated Collieries, Powell Duffryn Associated Collieries, National Coal Board, British Coal, Goitre Tower Anthracite Ltd

Maximum manpower/output:
**1930 – 650 men / 200,000 tons**
**1994 – 271 men / 707,000 tonnes**

Tower Colliery was so named due to its proximity to a tower built by ironmaster Francis Crawshay in 1848, which was his refuge from his workers during the upheavals of the mid-1800s. This drift was opened around 1864. It stayed with the Marquis of Bute until 1919 when it was sold to D.R. Llewellyn. It then had an estimated 150 million tons of coal reserves. In 1920 the Tower No. 2 was opened.

Along with the nation's other coal mines, Tower was nationalised in January 1947 and placed in the National Coal Board's South Western Division's No. 4 (Aberdare) Area, Group No. 2, employing 1,014 men. In April 1962 an explosion of methane gas killed nine miners at the pit. On 3 December 1974 flooding near the No. 4 pit from nearby opencast workings stopped all work on the N18 coalface in the Nine-Feet seam. The water was pumped out at a thousand gallons per minute, but it wasn't until 5 January 1975 that work recommenced.

Following the return to work after the 1984–85 miner's strike, the output of Mardy Colliery was diverted by underground roadway to Tower. Tower Colliery made a poor recovery after the strike, achieving only 68 per cent of production targets after a month; production from the V28 coalface was normal, but the V27 was giving poor results. Tower Colliery was the last British Coal mine to work in the South Wales Coalfield and was closed in April 1994.

However, the local NUM Lodge was determined to keep their pit open, and to provide employment in the Cynon Valley. They carried out an intense publicity campaign, lobbied Parliament and came away with a workers' buyout in which 239 men contributed £8,000 each out of their redundancy payments towards the buyout fund of £2,000,000. Under the name of Goitre Tower Anthracite Limited the mine was reopened and was a very successful enterprise, providing coal to power stations, British Steel, domestic and overseas markets until final closure in 2008.

The bleak, almost forbidding photo of the washery. Robert Fuller Courtesy Amgueddfa Cymru - National Museum Wales

A ranging drum shearer and
its operator in the 1990s

In near perfect conditions a locomotive hauls its load in 1990

The commercial end of the business – bagging the coal ready to deliver to households. **Courtesy R Tiley**

# TAFF VALE

Merthyr Tydfil stands proud at the northern end of the Taff Vale and indeed at the northern end of the South Wales Coalfield. Its bounteous reserves of iron, coal, limestone and water placed it at the forefront of the Industrial Revolution. Two of its ironworks, Cyfarthfa and Dowlais, were at one time the world's largest, and the owners, the Crawshays and the Guests, the world's richest people. This all started to unwind when steel replaced iron in the markets and new works nearer the coast became more profitable. But industry hadn't finished with Merthyr and the Taff Vale, and the area turned to selling its coal on the open markets. Such was the intensity of coal mining that by the 1930s most of the town's pits had closed and the area slumped into an era of deprivation that still exists today. Coal mining remained in the outer parts of the Merthyr Borough at such places as Treharris, Trelewis and at Merthyr Vale, and also further down the Vale at Abercynon, Albion, Nantgarw and New Rockwood.

GOING DOWN - Miners descending the shaft on the 21st of September 1981

# MERTHYR VALE COLLIERY | CLOSED 1989

Location: **Merthyr Vale / Aberfan**

Ordnance Survey grid reference/postcode:
SO 073000 / CF48 4RG

Operating dates: **1869–1989**

Depth: **495 yards**

Seams worked: **Four-Feet, Six-Feet, Seven-Feet, Nine-Feet, Gellideg, Yard, Five-Feet**

Owners: Nixon, Taylor, Cory, Nixon's Navigation Co., Llewellyn (Nixon) Ltd, Powell Duffryn Associated Collieries Ltd, National Coal Board

Maximum manpower/output:
**1902 – 3,064 men / 830,000 tons**

**Before the sinking of this colliery could start, the Taff River had to be diverted to provide sufficient room for the surface buildings.** In July 1876 owner John Nixon claimed that 'the quality of the coal – upper four feet smokeless – is said to be unsurpassed even by the Dowlais Company's Rhaslas coal, considered by many persons to be the best fuel in the South Wales basin'.

On nationalisation in 1947 Merthyr Vale Colliery was placed in the National Coal Board South Western Division's No. 4 Area, Group No. 4, and at that time employed 217 men on the surface and 843 men underground. In 1975 it won awards from the NCB and the European Architecture Heritage Year Business and Industrial Panel for being the tidiest pit in the UK. In 1976 it cost £500,000 to equip the B20 coalface, which made it the most expensive and sophisticated coalface in the South Wales Coalfield. In 1979 the B31 72-inch to 84-inch seams were the best-performing coalfaces in the seam thickness group in South Wales, and the mine produced 877 tonnes of coal per day. British Coal invested over £7 million in skip winding and high-tech coalface equipment and in 1988, 760 men produced 625,000 tonnes of coal from the Nine-Feet and Yard seams mostly for the Aberaman Phurnacite Plant to make smokeless fuel briquettes for the domestic market. Yet it was not enough to save it from the round of closures that came in 1989.

A general view of the colliery, taken after the pit closed

The winding engine house and headgear taken from the main road. **Robert Fuller Courtesy Amgueddfa Cymru - National Museum Wales**

The entrance road to the colliery with the sign post showing the way to the various sections. **Robert Fuller Courtesy Amgueddfa Cymru - National Museum Wales**

In 1981 it was working the Seven-Feet seam at a section of 173 cms, and the Five-Feet seam at 132cms

# ABERFAN

Suddenly at about 9.15 am on Friday 21 October 1966 the mine's waste tip started to collapse and began to rush down the mountain towards Aberfan. Two farm cottages halfway up the mountain were engulfed and the occupants killed, but the mass continued down the mountain until it covered eighteen houses and the Pantglas school. By the time it had stopped one hundred and forty-four men women and children had lost their lives. One hundred and sixteen of the victims were children, most of them between the ages of seven to ten years. One hundred and nine of them died in the Junior School.

Below: An aerial view of Aberfan
Opposite: Top and middle are Aberfan Cemetery with some of the headstones of the disaster victims
Bottom is the Memorial Garden

# TAFF BARGOED VALLEY

The Taff Bargoed Valley wriggles its way down from Bedlinog on to Trelewis, Treharris, Nelson and Quakers Yard, where it meets the Taff Vale and A470 road, 14 miles north of Cardiff. The reserves in the north of the valley were exploited by the Dowlais Iron Company from Bedlinog, Nantwen and Bedlinog Drift mines, which closed in 1924, 1930 and 1955 respectively. It was a different story in the mid-valley where Deep Navigation owned by the Ocean Company, Taff Merthyr – a joint venture between the Ocean and Powell Duffryn – and the NCB's Trelewis drift proved to be some of the most productive and were amongst the last to close in the Coalfield.

The control centre at Taff Merthyr Colliery

# TAFF MERTHYR COLLIERY | CLOSED 1993

Location: **Taff Bargoed Valley**

Ordnance Survey grid reference/postcode: ST 103990 / CF46 6RD

Operating dates: **1922–1993**

Depth: **1,903 feet**

Seams worked: **Four-Feet, Six-Feet, Seven-Feet, Nine-Feet**

Owners: Taff Merthyr Steam Coal Company, National Coal Board, British Coal

Maximum manpower/output:
**1930 – 1,450 men / 600,000 tons**
**1978 – 692 men / 350,000 tons**

Taff Merthyr Colliery was one of the most controversial mines in the South Wales Coalfield. The actions of some of the men, in dropping out of the South Wales Miners' Federation following what they thought was inept leadership during the 1926 strike, and their early return to work, created a bitterness between families and neighbours that lasted for decades. On the other hand, it was one of only five collieries in the whole of the UK at which no one returned to work early during the 1984–85 miners' strike.

It also had its share of firsts – such as when the first lodge of the newly formed South Wales Miners' Industrial Union was formed there – and lasts, when, along with Wyllie Colliery, it was the last deep mine to be sunk under private ownership in the South Wales Coalfield. It was also unique in that it was the only venture that the two giants – and rivals – of the Coalfield, the Ocean Coal Company and Powell Duffryn, worked together on. At a cost of over £10 million, two coalfaces were equipped with high-tech equipment with 590 men producing 650,000 tonnes of coal from the Seven-Feet Seam in 1988. In the week ending 14 May 1988 the pit reached the targeted 20,000 tonnes, but the period before that had been an anxious one with only the B23 district working between December and March. In September 1990 it set a Welsh output record for a week when the B24 Retreat Coalface advanced 234 feet 6 inches and produced 40,151 tonnes of coal for the power station market. Taff Merthyr Colliery was part of the mass closures announced by British Coal in late 1992 that caused such an uproar in Parliament, with public outcry and High Court injunctions following in its wake, all to no avail. By the time that confirmation of closure was made in May 1993, two-thirds of the men had already left. The last production shift was on 11 June 1993.

Trelewis Drift shared the same surface facilities as Taff. Trelewis was one of the most productive mines in the UK

This view taken from the east shows the colliery nestled into the Taff Bargoed Valley
**Creative Commons D O'Brien**

The coal preparation plant at Taff Merthyr, commonly called the washery
**Creative Commons D O'Brien**

The railway rapid loading station at Taff Merthyr but all the hi-tech equipment in the world couldn't save this colliery from closure

# SECTION 4

Section 4 covers four valleys - Rhymney Valley, Sirhowy Valley, Ebbw Valleys and Afon Lwyd Valley in an area from Penallta east to Blaenavon. The following pages feature a brief history of each pit and a selection of photographs, mainly from the National Museum of Wales, John Cornwell collection with some additional images from other sources.

---

1  **Penallta** – Hengoed
2  **Oakdale** – Blackwood
3  **Marine** – Cwm Ebbw Vale
4  **Blaenserchan** – Pontnewynydd, Pontypool
5  **Big Pit** – Blaenavon

# RHYMNEY VALLEY

Coal mining had been on a small scale at both ends of the Rhymney Valley until the 'coal boom' of the late 1800s, when the 'big boys' took over the interior. In 1883 Elliot's Colliery went down 1,600 feet, ten years later Universal Colliery was sunk to a depth of 1,960 feet, and finally in 1909 Bedwas Navigation Colliery became the deepest ever to be sunk in the valley at 2,585 feet.

Manpower figures became huge, with giants like Bargoed Colliery employing 2,823 men, Elliot's Colliery 2,757 and Llanbradach Colliery 2,246. Of course, everything has its price, and the price of coal was too often paid in blood; on 14 October 1913 an explosion at the Universal Colliery killed 439 men and boys in the worst mining disaster in British history.

When the Coal Industry Nationalisation Bill came into effect on 1 January 1947, the Rhymney Valley became the No. 5 Area of the South Western Division. It employed 8,750 men within the Rhymney Valley proper and 11,527 miners overall. Bedwas and Penallta Collieries were intended to be the long-term mining future within the valley, but the economic policies carried out by the Conservative government decided otherwise. Finally, the last deep mine to have worked in the Rhymney Valley, and indeed the last deep mine to have worked in the county of Caerphilly, Penallta Colliery was closed in 1990.

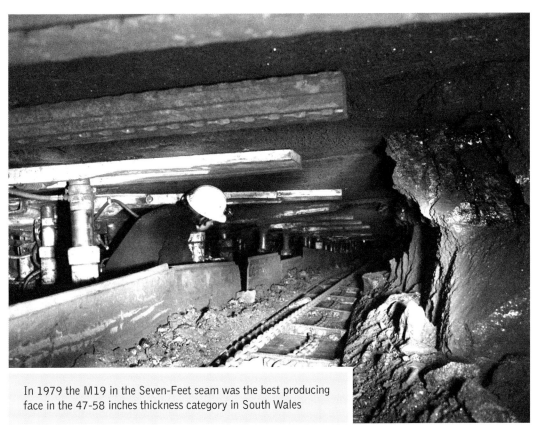

In 1979 the M19 in the Seven-Feet seam was the best producing face in the 47-58 inches thickness category in South Wales

# PENALLTA COLLIERY | CLOSED 1990

Location: **Hengoed**

Ordnance Survey grid reference/postcode:
ST 139957 / CF82 6AN

Operating dates: **1906–1990**

Depth: **2,400 feet**

Seams worked: **Red, Six-Feet, Rhas Las, Seven-Feet, Four-Feet**

Owners: Powell Duffryn, National Coal Board, British Coal

Maximum manpower/output:
**1931 – 3,208 men / 860,000 tons**

At Penallta Colliery, sinking of the two shafts was completed in 1909. The mineral take consisted of an area about two miles from east to west and three miles from north to south with the colliery approximately in the centre. It was originally sunk to a depth of 2,250 feet, with this pit being deepened to 2,400 feet in the 1950s. Both shafts were 21 feet in diameter and they were 70 yards apart.

On nationalisation of the country's coal mines in 1947, Penallta Colliery was placed in the National Coal Board South Western Division's No. 5 (Rhymney) Area, Group No. 5, and at that time employed 320 men on the surface of the mine and 1,614 men working in the Rhas Las (Upper-Nine-Feet), Seven-Feet, Six-Feet and Four-Feet seams. In 1969 this colliery was placed on the NCB's 'in jeopardy' list and warned that if production did not improve it would close. Uniquely in the history of the South Wales Coalfield, the NUM Lodge hired a public relations firm, PRS Publicity of Newport, and successfully fought off closure.

There was a setback in January 1987 when mine rescue teams battled for two days to put out an underground fire. Nevertheless, the colliery recovered and started to break its own productivity records, and in 1989 its single coalface in the Seven-Feet Seam produced 500,000 tonnes of coal. In 1990 the colliery produced 590,000 tonnes of saleable coal to feed Aberthaw Power Station.

Shortly afterwards, however, it was stated that the economically workable reserves of coal at Penallta Colliery had been exhausted. On 29 March 1991, at a special meeting, the workmen decided not to fight the closure, despite the NUM recommending that it should go through the review procedure.

Penallta in the 1920s. It was one of the first in South Wales to introduce mechanisation with Meco Moore loaders installed at the coalfaces

No.1 Pit, the downcast shaft, (foreground) was sunk to a depth of 2,349 feet, both shafts were 21 feet in diameter and were 70 yards apart

Both winding engines were housed in one building along with the electrical generators. This building measured 300 feet long by 70 feet wide

# SIRHOWY VALLEY

Industrially the Sirhowy Valley was dominated by the Tredegar Iron and Coal Company and their works and mines around Tredegar and Sirhowy. Eventually, when the coal seams were exhausted, they advanced further down the valley via Pochin, Markham, Oakdale and Wyllie collieries until they covered the deep-seam mineral rights of just over half the valley. The lower villages of the valley such as Ynysddu, Cwmfelinfach and Wattsville, with their accompanying mines of Nine Mile Point and Risca, eventually joined the Ocean Coal Company group before all the deep mines were acquired by the NCB in 1947. Deep mining stopped at both ends of the valley in the 1960s with the closure of Ty Trist and Nine Mile Point, Pochin, Wyllie and Risca collieries. Markham Colliery merged into the Oakdale Complex in the 1970s, leaving Oakdale as the last deep mine in the valley.

Alongside the big boys, numerous small levels littered the middle of the valley around Blackwood where the Mynyddislwyn seam outcropped. Such was the intensity of mining in this seam that it is now totally exhausted.

The three shafts in the 1950s, with the Waterloo Pit in the background. The upcast shaft is left and the downcast in the foreground

# OAKDALE NAVIGATION COLLIERY

Location: **Oakdale, Blackwood**

Ordnance Survey grid reference/postcode:
ST 184989 / NP12 4AB

Operating dates: **1907–1989**

Depth: **2,179 feet 7 inches**

Seams worked: **Old Coal, Meadow Vein, Big Vein, Rhas Las, Yard, Brithdir**

Owners: Oakdale Navigation Collieries Ltd (subsidiary of the Tredegar Iron and Coal Co.), National Coal Board, British Coal

Maximum manpower/output:
**1928 – 3,465 men\* / 1933 – 900,000 tons
1957 – 1,951 men / 599,138 tons**
*\*including Waterloo*

Oakdale Colliery had a difficult start to life when it encountered adverse geology in the pit-bottom area, amd what they had thought was the Rhas Las seam turned out to be an unworkable rider coal. However, the colliery was soon working the right seams and in 1913 employed 714 men. The pit then encountered a problem of a different kind: the Coalfield was booming and they found it difficult to recruit enough men, which resulted in them paying the highest wages in the Coalfield in 1915. There were further problems in 1932 when the colliery was found to be 'poaching' coal belonging to the neighbouring Crumlin Navigation Colliery, which resulted in 400 men being laid off.

On nationalisation in 1947 Oakdale Navigation Colliery was placed in the National Coal Board South Western Division's No. 6 (Monmouthshire) Area, Tredegar Group and at that time employed 320 men working at the surface and 1,772 men underground. In the late 1970s the NCB invested an estimated £35 million in a modernisation scheme, in which it was planned to merge Oakdale, Markham and Celynen North into one complex, which, it was claimed, would give a life of twenty years at 900,000 tonnes of coal production. In one week in November 1986 this pit recorded a production figure of 25,300 tonnes of coal, a pit record, but even production figures such as this were not enough to save it and it closed in 1989.

The middle tower is where the men were dropped 100 feet from the surface to the pit bottom. Behind the towers are baths and offices

The Waterloo Pit was the training pit for the No.6 Area, this photo shows the trainee's and instructors in the 1955. **Courtesy Amgueddfa Cymru - National Museum Wales**

The Waterloo was the only training pit in Wales for Bevin Boys during WWII. Mining trainees were taught here until 1970

Following re-organisation, it was planned to raise 6,500 tons of coal a day, with a planned annual output of 887,000 tons of coal

The afternoon shift waiting to go down in 1980

# EBBW VALLEYS

The Ebbw Valleys extend from the northern outcrop of the South Wales Coalfield at Ebbw Vale and Brynmawr down the twenty-odd miles to Risca at the southern crop of the field. In-between lies one of the world's most intensely mined areas. It all started at the northern end, where coal was needed to feed the ironworks at Ebbw Vale, Victoria, Beaufort, Nantyglo and Blaina, with the first pit being sunk in this area, at Ebbw Vale, being the Engine Pit in 1803.

At the other end mining started on a small scale at Waunfawr Colliery in 1799. When they discovered the celebrated Black Vein seam, which was about ten feet thick and of the best quality in the world, the mines crept into the centre of the valley and became bigger and deeper. Cwmtillery was sunk in the 1830s around the same time as the Black Vein Pit. Abercarn Colliery was deepened to the Black Vein in the 1860s, followed in the 1870s by others including the Celynen South, Llanhilleth, Roseheyworth and Waunlwyd, and then Risca, Marine, Six Bells, and on into the 1900s with Crumlin Navigation, Cwmcarn, Celynen North and Beynons. All this expansion came at a high price, with four explosions at Risca Black Vein killing 192 men and boys, one at Risca Colliery that killed 120 men and boys, and in 1878 at Abercarn Colliery the worst explosion in Monmouthshire, which killed 268 men and boys. There were many more such tragedies, leading up to the last one at Six Bells Colliery in 1960, which killed 45 men.

The OC4 coalface in October 1983

# MARINE COLLIERY | CLOSED 1989

**Location: Ebbw Fawr Valley**

Ordnance Survey grid reference/postcode:
SO 187043 / NP23 7TL

Operating dates: **1889–1989**

Depth: **1,254 feet**

Seams worked: **Four-Feet, Six-Feet, Seven-Feet, Nine-Feet**

Owners: Ebbw Vale Steel, Iron and Coal Co., Partridge, Jones & John Paton Ltd. National Coal Board, British Coal

Maximum manpower/output:
**1935 – 2,210 men / 600,000 tons**

At Marine in 1907, 3,044 lamps were drawn in one day, a world record at the time. Sadly, there were no St. David's Day celebrations on 1 March 1927 when an explosion at Marine Colliery killed 52 out of the 135 miners underground. Despite this tragedy life had to go on and in October 1929 the largest washery in the UK was constructed at Marine.

On nationalisation in 1947, Marine was placed in the National Coal Board's South Western Division's No. 6 (Monmouthshire) Area and at that time employed 289 men on the surface and 1,225 men working underground in the Old Coal, Black Vein and Big Vein seams. In January 1965 this colliery became the first in South Wales to have a remotely operated longwall coalface (ROLF) installed.

In 1977, following the link-up with Six Bells Colliery and that colliery's coal being diverted by underground roadway to Marine's shaft it was found that Marine was struggling to raise the production of both pits to the surface. Shaft capacity was increased to 300 tonnes of coal per hour by fitting double-decked cages at a cost of £90,000. However, production was still exceeding the shaft capacity and bunkers were installed underground, with the excess wound on the night shift.

In 1983 Marine Colliery was making £5.90 for every tonne of coal it produced, the third best performance in the South Wales Coalfield. Manpower at that time was 640 men. But on 3 March 1989, British Coal announced that Marine Colliery would close with the loss of 758 jobs. They blamed geological difficulties but stated that there would be no compulsory redundancies with all miners being offered jobs in other pits.

The colliery pictured from the east in the 1980s. The upcast shaft is on the left, and the downcast shaft is on the right

A general view in 1974, with a Western Class locomotive in the foreground, returning to Llanwern Steelworks following a delivery of ingots to the Ebbw Vale Works

This 800 tonne bunker eliminated the bottleneck in the shafts and output rose from 8,676 tonnes/week to 12,610 tonnes/week

On the right is a manriding belt (note the room above the bottom belt so that the men can sit up on it)

A hard heading in 1984. The heading had been bored and the workman is cleaning out the holes ready for shotfiring

# AFON LWYD VALLEY

The Afon Lwyd rises just above Blaenavon and makes its way down the valley, passing Pontypool, until after 13 miles it joins the River Usk at Caerleon. Along its way it coincides with the eastern limits of the South Wales Coalfield and its abundant supplies of coal and ironstone, as much as 30,000 tons per acre around the Varteg area. With the coal seams and ironstone veins coming to the surface they were first exploited by little scratchings, then by levels and slants and finally by shafts as the coal went deeper and deeper into the earth.

The collieries of the north and south of the valley were initially used to supply the great works at Blaenavon, Abersychan, Clydach and Pontypool, while Cwmbran Colliery in the south produced coal primarily for the Patent Nut and Bolt works in the town. Then the great export boom exploded on the scene and the deeper mines such as Tirpentwys, Blaenserchan and Llanerch came into being. Each of them is a record holder in its own way, even if some of those records are less desirable than others. The company that operated Tirpentwys had what must have been one of the longest names in the Coalfield: The Tirpentwys Black Vein Steam Coal and Coke Colliery Company Limited. Blaenserchan Colliery was the last deep mine to be worked in this valley and Llanerch Colliery had the unenviable record of experiencing the worst mining disaster in the valley in February 1890 when 176 men and boys died in an explosion of firedamp.

On the right side, in the middle, can be seen the sign showing the way to Blaenserchan from Marine a distance of 3½ miles

# BLAENSERCHAN COLLIERY

Location: **Pontnewynydd**

Ordnance Survey grid reference/postcode:
SO 245021 / NP4 6UN

Operating dates: **1890–1984**

Depth: **1,049 feet**

Seams worked: **Meadow Vein, Old Coal, Black Vein, Elled, Four-Feet, Three-quarter, Garw**

Owners: Partridge, Jones & Co., Partridge, Jones & John Paton Ltd, National Coal Board

Maximum manpower/output:
**1964 – 790 men / 182,000 tons**

This colliery was built across the valley from the old Llanerch Colliery and a shaft was sunk at Blaenserchan with the Llanerch shaft used as the downcast ventilating shaft. Sadly, there were no The second Blaenserchan shaft was sunk in 1915. The Blaenserchan Colliery shaft was originally sunk to the Five-Feet/Gellideg seam

and was elliptical in shape, 16 feet by 11 feet, but in 1899 it was deepened to 1,049 feet with the rest of the shaft being round and 18 feet in diameter.

The system of taking the coal to the washery was hampered by the steep contours of the valley. It was taken down by a zig-zag track to a tippler which dumped onto a conveyor which took it on to the washery. The coal was then washed, loaded into wagons and taken to the customer via the Cwmnantddu Valley. That was the case until 1947, when part of the Llanerch waste tip slid down into that valley and cut off the rail link. Instead of clearing the slip the railway line was diverted to the opposite side of the valley to Blaenserchan, the Llanerch Colliery side. Following the 1984–85 miners' strike it achieved 73 per cent of normal production despite some mechanical and electrical problems but this was still deemed unsatisfactory and Blaenserchan Colliery, the last deep mine to have worked in the Afan Lwyd Valley, closed on 28 August 1985.

The pit bottom in 1979 showing a tram of rubbish waiting to go up to the surface

A view during the 1970s re-organisation. The new fan is on the right. At the back is the main winding shaft

The cramped conditions at the surface of this mine can be seen in this photograph. With trams of coal passing within feet of buildings. The HSE would not be too happy with this layout!

# BIG PIT | CLOSED 1980

Location: **Blaenavon**

Ordnance Survey grid reference/postcode:
**SO 237087 / NP4 9XP**

Operating dates: **1880–1980**

Depth: **98 feet**

Seams worked: **Garw, Old Coal, Meadow Vein, Elled, Black Vein, Yard**

Owners: Blaenavon Iron & Coal Co. Blaenavon Co., National Coal Board; currently owned by National Museum of Wales

Maximum manpower/output:
**1960 – 1,526 men / 307,000 tons**

In 1880 the Blaenavon Iron and Coal Company Limited reorganised many of the old workings in the Forge Side area and formed the Big Pit. These included the Coity Pit (No. 3 pit), which was sunk in 1840 and became the Big Pit upcast shaft. It was 135 feet deep and nine feet in diameter. Kearsley's Pit, which was deepened from the Three-Quarter Seam at a depth of 128 feet to the Old Coal seam at a depth of 293 feet, was originally sunk in 1800 and was five feet in diameter. The Nos. 1 and 2 pits were sunk between 1860 and 1863 to the Three-Quarter Seam and were deepened in 1897 to the Old Coal Seam.

Following nationalisation, the NCB decided to place the whole of the mineral take in the Blaenavon area, including the collieries of Big Pit, Garn Slope, Kay's Slope and Vipond's Colliery into one super-pit, which they called Blaenavon. It was believed this would extend the mining life of the area by thirty years, and from that time all the men were to descend down Big Pit rather than any of the other shafts. Prior to closure on 4 April 1980 the output per manshift on the coalface was 3.3 tonnes and overall for the colliery it was 1.1 tonnes.

Following closure, Torfaen Borough Council purchased the site for £1 and in conjunction with funding from the Wales Tourist Board and the European Union amounting to £1.5 million it was reopened to visitors in 1983, employing 71 people. In 2001 it came under the control of the National Museum of Wales and is now called Big Pit National Mining Museum of Wales. It has become of the top tourist attractions in Wales, offering free admission and including an underground tour as well as attractions on the surface

A timeless view of Big Pit with Blaenavon in the background

It's June 1979 and the afternoon shift are getting dressed by the bath's dirty side lockers

The colliery safety officer, **Bill Gunter**, inspecting the G11 coalface in 1979

In 1973 a drift, 1,860 feet long, dipping down at between 1:6 to 1:4 was driven from the washery

This time **Bill Gunter** is at the entrance to Dick Kear's Slope which was part of Big Pit

Pit props being loaded into trams for use at the coalface. Note the adapted trams made to carry the steel arches

The last NCB manager of Big Pit, **Glyn Morgan**, says farewell in November 1980

# MACHINERY

These photographs have been chosen to give the reader a feel for the size and complexity of some of the major pieces of equipment and infrastructure employed underground to help the miners extract coal on an industrial scale.

A ranging drum shearer being tested on the 3rd of July 1972

In May 1980, an electrician inspects electrical switchgear at Oakdale Colliery

A charging station for electric locomotives at Oakdale Colliery

The very large bucket of an Eimco
Shovel shown by cap lamp light in 1980

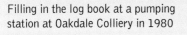

Filling in the log book at a pumping
station at Oakdale Colliery in 1980

The steel rope comes off the drum, out of the
building, over the pulley wheels on the headgear,
and then onto the cage

# PIT PONIES

This selection of pit ponies shows them at work above and below ground and their often proud handlers showing them off to the camera.

A superb underground photo of a horse and his handler at Lady Windor Colliery

This one was taken at Tower Colliery and shows the horse hitched to a single supply tram

Trekking across the surface of Big Pit this photograph typifies the bond that develops between horse and handler

This photo was taken at Lewis Merthyr in 1909. Collieries took great pride in entering their 'show' horses into competitions. **Courtesy Amgueddfa Cymru - National Museum Wales**

# MISCELLANEOUS PHOTOGRAPHS FROM AROUND THE COLLIERY

## THE MINER'S STRIKE OF 1985

A selection of images from the strike showing not only some action on the front line but also the support from wives and the community. With a reminder from years gone by.

The 1984/85 strike and police massed at the entrance to the Celynen South Colliery

If the police marched 'in step' then most miners believed that they were soldiers

It is 1929 and three 'scabs' are escorted through King Edward Street, Blaengarw by a few 'Bobbies'

Food, clothing, toys and donations came from all over the world, this donation was a bit nearer to home! **Courtesy Binny Jones**

A bric a brac sale at Maerdy. The wives of miners matched their husbands in their determination to keep jobs

Cwm Lodge picketing at Aberthaw Power Station; R. Jones, P. Shepard and G. Winogorski

Penallta Colliery miners demonstrating in Cardiff in 1984

The backbone of any colliery, the blacksmith's, they could repair anything with next to nothing

Inspecting the shaft-one of the most dangerous jobs in the colliery. Note the harness & safety chain attached to the chain of the cage

Testing for methane gas with a methanometer, a more reliable way than using a flame safety lamp

Coke coming out of Coedely Coke Ovens for Port Talbot steel works in 1983

# NOTES AND GLOSSARY

On going to the lamp room at the start of his shift the underground worker would place the lamp check into a box designed for the purpose. The lamp room attendant would then enter the number on the check as being in work, and would hang the check on a hook next to the man's battery charger. At the end of the shift the miner would replace his electric cap lamp on the charger and collect his lamp check, indicating that he had finished his shift and left the mine.

## National Coal Board (NCB)

The National Coal Board was formed on 12 July 1946 to take control of the British coal industry. On Vesting Day, 1 January 1947, around 800 private colliery companies were brought under state control and operated by the NCB. The NCB became British Coal in 1987, with Britain's coal industry being privatised in 1997.

## Imperial tons and metric tonnes

Following its formation in 1947 the NCB used the measurement called the (imperial) ton to weigh its coal. The ton weighed in at 20 hundredweights or 2,240 pounds. In 1969 the government set up the metrification board to convert imperial measurements to metric units. The UK joined the European Economic Union in 1973 and in doing so agreed to the conversion to metric standards. The NCB converted from the old ton to the metric tonne of 1,000 kilogrammes. The imperial ton was approximately 1,016 kilograms.

## Feet and metres

All sinking logs with regards to the depths of shafts and the thickness of coal seams were recorded in feet and inches, or in yards, feet and inches. Even today this is the generally accepted measurement used when discussing shafts and seams in South Wales and is the measurement used in this book, with the inches rounded to the nearest foot.

A MANRIDING TRAIN READY TO DESCEND CWMGWILI SLANT

# A Glossary of Local/Mining Terms

**Adit:** A drainage tunnel

**Bank/Banksman**: The top of the pit/the man who controls the shaft operations from the surface.

**Belts**: The system of conveyors that carry the coal to pit bottom.

**Blackdamp**: Carbon monoxide that gathers in poorly ventilated areas.

**Bond**: The carriage that travels through the shaft.

**Bottoms**: The floor of a tunnel that has been pushed up by pressure.

**Box end:** The tail end of a conveyor

**Brattice cloth:** A material that was hung in roadways to redirect airflow.

**Bull week:** The week before a holiday in which a miner aimed to earn as much as possible.

**Bumpers**: Small noises or 'bangs' within the coal.

**Button boy:** A conveyor attendant

**Butty**: Originally a puddler's assistant in the ironworks, later an assistant or mate.

**Cage**: Another name for the carriage that travels the shaft.

**Cap lamp:** The main system of lighting for the miner. The 'torch' or cap lamp was attached to the miner's helmet, with its battery strapped to the miner's waist belt.

**Captain**: The leader of a coalface team, but not management.

**Carriers**: Conveyor belts.

**Checkweigher**: Pre-nationalisation, a man elected and paid by the miners to ensure that their trams of coal were correctly registered for payment.

**Chock**: Coalface roof support.

**Clanny**: A type of safety lamp.

**Cog blocks:** Timber used to support the waste side of the advancing roadway.

**Collier**: The man who cuts and fills the coal.

**Comp**: Industrial injury benefit.

**Count boy:** The person who goes round the coalface writing down the amount of work each collier has done.

**Crawley**: An armoured conveyor made in Crawley.

**Cross measure:** A tunnel that travels from one seam to another.

**Cross cut:** A tunnel that joins two other tunnels together.

**Cutter**: The machine that cuts the coal.

**Davy lamp:** An early type of safety lamp for use in flammable atmospheres (invented by Sir Humphrey Davy in 1815).

**Deputy**: The official in charge of safety in a district, originally called a fireman.

**Disc**: A type of coal cutter.

**District**: The area of coal extraction, normally subdivided into coalfaces.

**Docket**: The miner's pay slip.

**Doggie haulier:** The man in charge of the underground transport system.

**Doorboy**: A person employed in the old days to open ventilation doors to allow trains to pass through.

**Doubler**: The working of two consecutive shifts.

**Downcast shaft:** The pit that takes the fresh air down into the mine.

**Drams**: The wagons that carried the coal underground. Also called trams and tubs, they varied from holding one to two tonnes each.

**Drivage**: Normally a single tunnel 'driven' into a new area of working.

**Drifts**: Tunnels that are 'driven' down or upwards.

**Dump road:** The tunnel that the coal is conveyed in.

**Engineman**: The person who drives a haulage engine.

**Engine plane:** The tunnel that a particular haulage engine traverses.

**Fireman**: The early name for a deputy. Derived from his duty of detecting gas and 'firing' small amounts.

**Face**: The place where the coal is extracted.

**Faceworker**: The modern name for a collier.

**Falls**: Collapses of the roof.

**Faults**: Geological disturbances.

**Four-Feet**: The ready cut length of wooden roof supports; could Also be Five-Feet, Three-Feet, etc.

**Firedamp**: The explosive methane gas.

**Fire doors:** Doors used to prevent any fire from spreading throughout the mine

**Garforth lamp:** The relightable safety lamp carried by officials to detect gas.

**Gas**: Methane.

**Gate end:** One end of a coalface.

**Goaf/Gob**: The empty area where the coal has been extracted.

**Grub**: Food.

**Guides**: The attachments in the shaft that the carriages run on – can be either rigid rails or flexible ropes depending on how 'true' the shaft was sunk.

**Headgear**: The framework and pulley sited above the shaft.

**Heading and stall system:** An old system of coal extraction where the coal was taken from the headings and coal pillars were left behind to form roof supports.

**Headings**: Another name for tunnels.

**Hitcher**: The man who controls operations At the bottom of the shaft.

**Inbye**: A term relative to position, meaning nearer to the coalface, and opposite to the term outbye. Sometimes it is used on the surface to mean that an individual is in the mine.

**Jigger**: An early form of metal face conveyor.

**Journey**: An underground train, normally consisting of around 24 trams.

**Laggings**: Timber placed behind steel arches to prevent debris falling through.

**Lamp check:** The numbered metal disc left in the lamp room when a miner takes his cap lamp underground.

**Lamp room:** The surface building where miners collect their safety and cap lamps, it was also the place where their 'time' was booked. A lamp station was a place underground where the old flame lamps could be relit.

**Levels**: Collieries that were driven directly into the coal seams without the need of pits.

**Lock-out**: Pre-nationalisation system where the old coal owners would lock the colliery gates and prevent the men from working until they agreed to whatever the owners had demanded.

**Lodge**: A branch of the South Wales Miners' Federation.

**Lodge room:** An entry in the side of a shaft where a pump was deposited.

**Longwall**: A system of coal extraction.

**Main gate:** The end of a coalface where the coal comes out.

**Mandril**: A miner's pickaxe.

**Main and tail:** A type of two-drummed haulage engine.

**Measures**: The coal-bearing rock series.

**Miners' agent:** A full-time elected miners' representative who looked after a number of lodges.

**Miners' fortnight:** The annual holidays.

**Nine-Feet**: Can refer to the heavy timbers used for roof support, or more commonly to the size of the steel arches used for tunnel roof support. They came in varying sizes such as 12 feet, 18 feet, etc.

**Norm**: The basic amount of work required from a collier before extra money could be earned.

**Notes**: Authorisation by an official for a man to ascend the shaft early. They came for various reasons but mainly for working in wet conditions or for carrying heavy items in or out of the coalface.

**Opencast**: A method of mining in which coal is extracted at or from a level near the earth's surface, rather than from a shaft.

**Ostler**: A man who works with horses.

**Outburst**: The phenomenon of gas pressure forcing coal to blow out into a working place.

**Outbye**: A word relative to position, meaning farther from the coalface, opposite to inbye. It is loosely used at times by miners to signify the surface.

**Outcrop**: Where the coal seams come to or near the surface.

**Pack/Packer**: The stone or timber wall at the ends of a coalface used to support the roof and to direct ventilation.

**Panel**: An area of coal to be worked.

**Panzer**: A German-made armoured face conveyor.

**Pillars**: Sections of coal left intact to support the roof.

**Plough**: A type of coal cutter and filler.

**Posts**: Roof supports.

**Price list:** The complex series of items that a collier would be paid for.

**Props**: Roof supports, mostly of the steel or hydraulic types.

**Ranging drum shearer:** A coal cutter and filler.

**Repairs**: Maintenance of the tunnels to the correct dimensions.

**Retreat system:** Where two roadways are driven to the far end of the coal reserves and the coalface worked back towards the pit bottom.

**Return**: The tunnel that the used air travels through on its way back to the shaft.

**Rib**: The coal on the outsides of the coalface that is not being worked.

**Rider**: The man who accompanies journeys to their destination.

**Rider coal:** A thin seam of coal above the main seam

**Rippings/Ripper**: The advancing of the tunnels either side of a coalface.

**Roads**: Tunnels.

**Scraper chain:** A type of armoured conveyor.

**Shackler**: The person who makes up a journey by joining the trams together with shackles.

**Shearer**: A type of coal cutter and filler.

**Shot firing:** The use of explosives to advance a tunnel.

**Sinking**: The process of opening a shaft.

**Skips**: A type of container for holding coal during winding in the shafts.

**Slants**: Tunnels driven from the surface into the coal seams.

**Sprags**: Pieces of shaped wood placed in the wheels of trams to stop them.

**Squeese**: Geological pressure forcing the roof or floor to close in.

**Stables**: Places to house/turn machinery at the end of coalfaces.

**Stalls**: Workplaces for extracting coal.

**Stent**: A length of a coalface allocated to a collier. Could be around seven yards long.

**Sump**: The part of the shaft below the pit bottom usually used for storing/pumping water.

**Take**: The area of coal extraction.

**Tail gate:** The opposite side of a coalface to the main gate.

**Team**: The men of a coal production unit on a coalface.

**Tip end:** The place where one conveyor tips onto another, or into trams.

**Tommy box:** Food container.

**Trams**: Underground wagons.

**Trumps**: The old payment that a collier would pay to his assistant.

**Tubs**: Underground wagons.

**Turnover**: The system of moving the coalface conveyor forward once the coal had been extracted for that shift.

**Under the chippings:** Leaving a coal roof.

**Upcast**: The shaft in which the stale air is extracted.

**Walking chocks:** Coalface roof supports

**Winder**: The machinery that brings men, coal and materials through the shaft.

**Yardage**: Piecework for colliers where they are paid for the distance that they go forward.